The Incentive Cure
The Real Relief For Health Care

François de Brantes

Co-author: Bob Conte
Cover Design: John Milano
Illustrations: Kriss Wittmann
References & Edits: Jenna Sirkin

ISBN 978-0-9884381-2-5

"The cause of runaway health costs is malpractice, but not the medical kind. Rather, we're guilty of business model malpractice on a grand scale."

– Clayton Christensen, Professor, Harvard Business School

"It's tough to do right when you're encouraged to do wrong."

– François de Brantes, Executive Director, Health Care Incentives Improvement Institute

Table of Contents

Foreword

Bob Conte and I started our journey into this weird world of health care about 20 years ago, when we were both working for a marketing communications firm in Massachusetts. One day we found ourselves in a meeting with one of our corporate clients. Our assignment was to create a campaign explaining some health care benefit changes to the company's retirees. We spent the next several hours sitting in a conference room, understanding maybe one of every three words being spoken. Acronyms were thrown around like bets in a casino, and far faster. As we struggled to keep up, we asked ourselves for the first, but certainly not the last time: Why does this stuff have to be so complicated?

Since then we've invented some acronyms of our own, and the version of English we heard all those years ago has become my first language. More importantly, we've learned that behind the babble are some simple hard truths that the health care industry has long tried to ignore or hide. It's taken me more than a decade to fight through the fog, by constantly asking the basic question that every child asks and every parent has heard countless times: Why? Why aren't patients getting the right care? Why does America spend twice as much per person as the next biggest spender? Why do the rules that apply to every other industry not apply to health care? Why? Why? Why?

These are the same questions you may be asking yourself today. It's taken us a while to get to the answers, and this is our attempt to provide them to you.

We started out with the same basic knowledge most Americans have, and learned as we went along. While many of these questions were met with the same blank stare and non-answer parents often give — "because that's the way it is"— we've learned that, in fact, it doesn't have to be this way.

While Bob continued to pursue a career as a business writer and communications consultant, I have devoted mine to developing real answers to these many questions, and I know that many of the big problems can and will be solved if we all play our roles. It won't be quick or easy, but the cure is in reach. We hope that is what you take away from this book.

François de Brantes
Newtown, Connecticut
December 2012

Introduction

In September 2012, the Institute of Medicine (IOM), a division of the non-profit, non-partisan National Academy of Sciences that's well respected in policy circles, released a report stating that *30 cents of every dollar spent on health care is wasted.*[1] That's about $750 billion (an amount roughly comparable to the annual Defense Department budget) flowing into the health care industry each year and providing no benefit to those receiving the care or spending the money.

That would be your employer, your government, your insurance company, and, worst of all, you.

How did we get here? In our view, with apologies to James Carville: It's the incentives, stupid. Everything that happens in health care today – the way physicians and hospitals are organized, the way insurance plans operate, the way medical devices and pharmaceuticals move through the supply chain, the way consumers access and receive care – is driven by financial incentives that are often perverse, and at worst plainly destructive.

After all, waste on this scale doesn't happen by itself. It happens for very specific reasons.

* * *

What is an incentive? On the simplest level, it's a force that encourages a person or an organization to take one action instead of another. Some incentives whisper, some incentives scream, but their power to influence behavior and shape markets is undeniable.

rational individuals* * *

Every day, millions of health care workers wake up and get ready to offer one of the noblest of services – to try and heal and bring comfort to the sick. This book is in no way an indictment of their motives or professionalism. They do valiant work, day in and day out, even as they confront extrinsic incentives that chip away at their mission and souls.

What do we mean by *"extrinsic incentives?"*

Consider this scenario. You're driving a year-old car, and the engine light pops on. The car is under full warranty, so you bring it into the dealer. The problem is fixed quickly at no charge. This simple interaction between the buyer and provider of a service illustrates the broader and essential role of extrinsic (external) and intrinsic (internal) incentives. *if we have the means, what ab extrinsic strum? i.e. basic needs*

[Intrinsically, most of us want to do the right thing for ourselves, personally and professionally. You want to maintain the car well, so it retains its value and gets you safely from one place to another.] The dealer wants to do the best possible job to keep you happy, so you'll buy from him again. If the car is serviced well and doesn't need extra repairs, he does well and so do you. *delayed gratification*

Often, however, it doesn't work this way. You may ignore that engine light, especially if your warranty has run out. Maybe you don't know much about cars, and you're concerned the dealer will take advantage and do unnecessary work. In fact, you may be right. The shop makes money on any repair, however small. It may indeed find something else to fix, as long as it's broadly within the bounds of reason. In any case, you don't want to risk it. And so a small problem festers and eventually grows into something much worse.

You can substitute pretty much any other product or service, and the core issue is the same: extrinsic incentives can get in the way of intrinsic incentives. The trick is to avoid the misalignment as much as possible. It's a difficult balance, one that sociologist Frederick Herzberg worked through in his theory on motivation.[2] His premise is simple: *Minimize the factors that lead to bad/negative behaviors, and the positive motivators will assert themselves.* Indeed, when applied to health care, the basic principles are almost absurdly simple, at least in theory.

Need to reduce waste? Remove the financial and legal incentives for providers to perform as many tests and procedures as possible, and financially engage the patient in health care service purchasing decisions.

Need to make the sickest, costliest patients healthier? Remove incentives for physicians to ignore one another, so patients with chronic conditions receive the coordinated treatment proven to deliver better results. And remove the incentives for patients to delay getting needed care or taking the steps to improve personal health habits.

Need to make hospitals safer? Remove incentives to ignore the problem by collecting and publicly displaying safety records. Restaurants and workplaces are often obligated to post their safety ratings on the front door. Why not hospitals?

Need to build a real functioning market? Remove incentives for sellers to keep the actual costs of medical goods and services hidden, so buyers can compare prices and make informed choices. info/understand gap

Freed from these types of negative incentives, there's no question that clinicians, consumers and other industry players would assert their positive behaviors. We're going to show you how.

Of course, if we're right, it begs the question: Why haven't these solutions been implemented?

Again, the answer is simple. The agents of the status quo, who profit massively from the inefficiencies and waste of health care resources, don't really want clinicians and consumers to change their behaviors. They don't want anyone to administer a cure, because they're reaping substantial benefits – $750 billion worth – by keeping the system as it is, sick.

After all, if behaviors changed, if the negative extrinsic incentives were neutralized, fewer pills would be bought, fewer unnecessary procedures performed, fewer devices implanted in bodies. And those who sell all that stuff would be unhappy. You can't "unbloat" an industry of this size without someone losing out. But here's the important point. The American consumer would win, and so would every business struggling to pay health insurance premiums, and so would the nation at large. And billions of dollars in wasted resources could find a more purposeful use.

* * *

In any discussion of the health care industry's failings, there's bound to be a certain amount of emotional conflict. Many of us love our doctors. We marvel at the medical advances that allow us to live longer and healthier lives. We appreciate the skill and devotion of those who care for our aging parents or other loved ones.

Yet we've all received medical bills we can't understand. We've all sat in the doctor's office and filled out the same forms again and again. We've all fought with physicians, hospitals, pharmacies or insurance companies over seemingly simple matters. We've all received expensive services we probably didn't need. We've all paid wildly different prices for the exact same services based on whatever coverage we happened to have (or not have). We've all known someone who went into the hospital and came out a whole lot sicker. And we've all behaved in self-destructive ways – eating badly, not exercising enough, and ignoring the doctor's advice.

Economists, who typically agree on very little, agree that our health care spending puts us on a clear path to financial ruin. It also represents a huge transfer of resources from the young to the old, threatening the promises we've made to future generations. As much as any foreign enemy, real or imagined, it presents a clear and present danger to our national well-being.

SSI insolvent ~ 2030

There's plenty of shared blame to go around among policy makers, insurers, physicians, hospitals, and patients. And so we all must do our part to apply the cure. But real and lasting change won't happen until the incentives change. The good news: A great deal of experimentation is underway in American health care, much of it below the radar of the general public. Attitudes within the industry are changing. The foundations of real markets, with transparent price and quality information, are being constructed. Fresh ideas are being piloted. And at long last, just as companies in other industries have always put the needs of customers first, health insurers and health care providers are slowly breaking free of their self-imposed bureaucratic shackles and putting patients at the center.

In this book, we attempt to summarize these initiatives, the thinking behind them, and what these changes mean to every American. The hand wringers in the ivory towers will accuse us of over-simplifying, but that's ok. After all, the industry has been over-complicating things for way too long, and we're all paying the price for it. It's time to simplify and get things done.

Our goal is to arm you with the truth and with solutions, and give you a call to action.

As consumers, we all need to understand the forces at work (both for us and against us), so we can make smarter decisions about our care, and be more mindful in our interactions with physicians and hospitals. Ask your doctor why that test or procedure is necessary. Find out what it costs before you agree. Maybe you can get the same quality treatment at a lower cost (for example, an MRI at an imaging center instead of a hospital). Don't go for the brand name drug if the generic works just as well for you. Over time, each of these actions will cause one small ripple of change that, when combined with millions of others, can make a real difference – become the real cure the system needs.

And by all means, write to your state's legislators and congressional representatives, call them, visit them in their offices, and ask them why they have refused to significantly reduce the negative incentives that plague health care. They need to do their part as much as you do, and you're the one who will have to push them. And if they waffle, if they duck, kick the bums out, because you and your children deserve a lot better.

Glossary of Key Terms:

Providers – the common term for those who provide health care services, such as physicians, nurses, hospital staff, home health agencies, etc.

Health Plans – are insurers. They contract with providers and pay them according to the terms of those contracts for services that are a covered benefit of the insured.

Payers – are those who process and pay claims submitted by providers. For the most part, payers are public and private sector health plans. For example, Medicare and Medicaid are public sector payers; Aetna, UnitedHealthcare, and the Blue Cross Blue Shield plans are all private sector payers.

Purchasers – are those who buy health insurance. All companies that offer health insurance benefits to employees are purchasers. Every year, they look for health plans that can administer those health benefits. Local, state and federal governments are also purchasers for their employees' and retirees' health benefits.

The Role Of Charitable Foundations

It is a testimony to how badly health care is screwed up that over a dozen large and well-funded charitable foundations are fully devoted to providing grants and other financial support to develop some fixes.

Among the more notable are the Robert Wood Johnson Foundation, based in New Jersey and created by the founder of Johnson & Johnson products; the Commonwealth Fund, based in New York; the West Foundation, based in San Diego and created by the founder of Qwest Communications; and the Kaiser Family Foundation, based in California and created by the founders of Kaiser Industries.

Many other foundations were created when not-for-profit hospitals or health plans were either purchased by, or changed their status to, for-profit organizations. Typically, as part of that conversion, certain proceeds from the sale must be placed into a new foundation that will serve the needs of the population in that state. Notable ones include the California Healthcare Foundation, the Colorado Health Foundation, and the New York State Health Foundation.

Collectively, these foundations have assets well in excess of $20 billion and distribute millions of dollars each year to researchers, communities, and special projects, all of which are focused on improving the affordability and quality of health care and improving the lives of patients. They publish reports on the work they've done, and try and spread the lessons learned, especially to policymakers in states and Washington DC.

Much of the work funded by these organizations has helped shed light on the causes of the problems in health care and some of the solutions to those problems. Many of our references in this book come from work conducted by these Foundations or organizations they support.

Chapter 1 – The Shape We're In

American exceptionalism

When it comes to health care, America is certainly exceptional, but mostly in the wrong ways. *We spend twice as much per person as any other country, our health outcomes are average, and the growth in health care insurance premiums is causing average family incomes to stagnate.*

Spending – No other advanced country spends as much on health care products and services for its people, or gets less value in return for those dollars. Not even close. In the U.S., health care consumed just 6% of U.S. economic output in 1965. By 1990, that figure had doubled to 12%. Today, it's 18%.[3] In most industrialized countries, health expenditures consume about 9% of economic output … half as much as we do.

Figure 1. Growth in National Health Expenditures and Average Tax Share as % of Gross Domestic Product

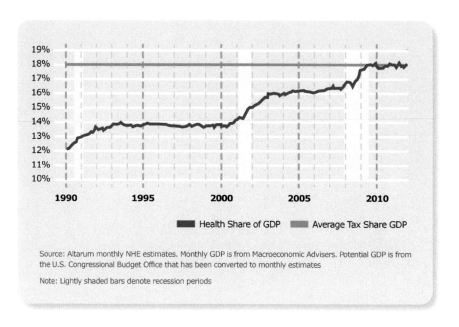

Source: Altarum monthly NHE estimates. Monthly GDP is from Macroeconomic Advisers. Potential GDP is from the U.S. Congressional Budget Office that has been converted to monthly estimates

Note: Lightly shaded bars denote recession periods

To put it in perspective, 18% is roughly equivalent to the average amount the U.S. Treasury has collected in taxes in recent decades (depicted by the orange line in Figure 1). In other words, if the U.S. government paid for all the health expenses in the country, every single cent of the taxes it collected would go to that one purpose. Nothing would be left over for roads, for schools, for defense, or anything else. Health care would eat up all of it.

Fortunately the government "only" pays about 45% of our total health care costs, with the balance paid by employers and individuals.[4] That still means a huge chunk of our tax dollars are used to pay for health care, mostly for older or lower income Americans through Medicare and Medicaid. And if the rate of increase continues, the portion of health care spending that has to be covered by taxes will go up, crowding out everything else. Between health care, Social Security and interest on the national debt, there will be virtually no money left over to pay for any other government program. As such, we have to find a way to control the rate of spending increase.

Given this high level of spending, you might assume that Americans are at least receiving better care than citizens of other nations. Not so. The hard truth is that the U.S. lags well behind other advanced nations in delivering timely and effective care. *In fact, given that we have the world's most powerful economy, our performance on many health care measures is dismal.*

Outcomes – Recent statistics from the World Health Organization show that from infant mortality to life expectancy – literally from cradle to grave – health outcomes in the U.S. are mediocre compared to other developed nations. In a 2006 study, the United States was number one in terms of health care spending per capita but ranked 39th for infant mortality, 43rd for adult female mortality, 42nd for adult male mortality, and 36th for life expectancy.[5]

A Commonwealth Fund report from 2010 puts it this way: "Despite having the most costly health system in the world, the United States consistently underperforms on most dimensions of performance, relative to other countries ... Compared with six other nations—Australia, Canada, Germany, the Netherlands, New Zealand, and the United Kingdom—the U.S. health care system ranks last or next-to-last on five dimensions of a high performance health system: quality, access, efficiency, equity, and healthy lives."[6]

Another report compares health care spending, supply, utilization, prices, and quality in 13 industrialized countries.[7] Of these, the U.S. spends far more on health care than any other country. The findings suggest that this higher spending cannot be attributed to higher incomes, an older population, or greater utilization of hospitals and doctors. Instead, the main reason we spend more on health care is simply because ... our health care costs more.

The U.S. also lags behind in an area we should be great at: Electronic health records (EHR) technology. You might assume we'd lead the world here, given our record of innovation in computers, software and the Internet. Yet many providers still operate in the primitive realm of paper records and handwritten prescriptions. Compared to doctors in other advanced nations, American primary care doctors are well behind in adopting electronic health records or prescribing medications electronically.[8] This makes it harder to coordinate care, adhere to standard clinical guidelines, and identify errors. (Those pen and paper scripts, often scribbled in haste, remain a notorious cause of drug errors, sometimes for the simple reason that the pharmacist can't read them.)

All these poor outcomes have contributed to the very high growth in spending, which in turn has led to very rapid increases in health insurance premiums.

Premiums – All health care services, whether valuable or not, whether directly linked to improving outcomes or simply wasteful, are usually paid for. Some are paid by the federal or state governments through Medicare and Medicaid, and many are paid by health insurance companies covering their plan members. All these costs add up for any individual, and across individuals in a population, and can be calculated as an average cost per person.

Clearly, not everyone uses the same amount of services, just as not everyone has an auto accident, or a house fire. Nevertheless, total costs for a specific population insured by a company, divided by the number of covered individuals, is equal to the insurance premium paid by (or on behalf of) a plan member. Typically, in most companies, the employer pays a portion of the premium, and the employee pays a portion. In the past decade, premium costs have skyrocketed as health care expenses have continued to rise. And here's the real rub. What's risen most is not the amount of services delivered per person, but the price.[9] So while in most other industries competition has led to prices going down (think of how much less it costs to buy a large screen TV today than ten years ago), in health care prices have kept going up. As a result, employees and employers are paying a lot more in insurance premiums now than in 2000.[10]

Figure 2: Increase in Health Insurance Premiums

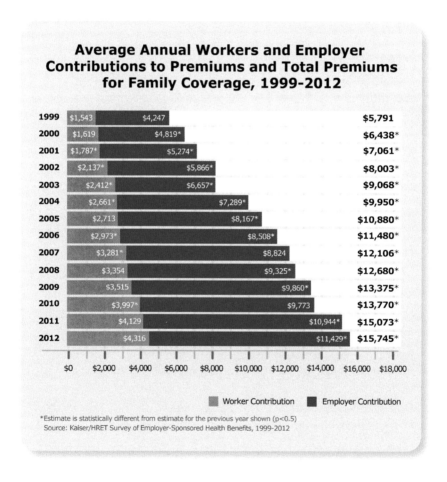

Benefits, including health insurance, are simply part of the total cost of compensation for an individual employee. So when an employer looks at people costs in a company, she adds up the salary, any potential bonuses, health insurance, other insurance, and any other benefit such as retirement plan contribution. Figure 2 shows that since 1999 employers have had to pay out $7,000 more per employee in health insurance premiums.10 Consider then that if premiums hadn't risen, that money might have been paid out in higher salaries instead.

The real cost of premium increases

Newtown, CT, is much like any small town in the U.S. The total budget for its schools has grown faster than the rest of the municipal budget, and now stands at a whopping $68 million, in a town whose total population is close to 28,000.

Since 2008, even before the Great Recession, the budget presented by the town has been soundly rejected, leading to revisions and a spate of referenda. This budget circus intensified during and after the recession, and continues to this day. The message from the residents is quite simple: No more tax increases. With stagnating household incomes (see next story), property tax increases mean less disposable cash and further downward pressure on residential home prices. And we simply can't afford it anymore. We need breathing room, and forcing the town to adopt a zero-based budgeting (no increases) should provide that breathing room over time.

But here's the hitch. There's a piece of the municipal budget that simply keeps climbing: The health insurance premiums for the municipal workers, including the teachers and school staff. In fact, of the $68 million total budget for the schools, $10.5 million (or 15%) is for health insurance costs. Those costs have been rising, on average, by 10%

in our area, which means over $1 million a year in added costs.

So here's the simple math. Health care costs go up by $1 million, but the budget stays the same. That means $1 million in the budget has to be cut to make room for that increase. So what's going to go? A couple of the non-tenured teachers, some of the retiring staff that isn't replaced, and whatever supplies and other operating expenses that can be cut. And the following year, another million, and another, and so on.

The problem in Newtown is the same as everywhere else: Increases in health care spending are crowding out other expenses, and forcing other parts of the budget to be cut back. And let's say that residents allowed a 1.5% increase in the school budget. That would amount to just about $1 million, and would only cover the increase in health insurance premiums, nothing else. So as buildings get older, they can't be repaired. As salaries try to grow, they either need to be contained, or folks have to be laid off. That's the true math of ever-increasing premiums that we can no longer afford.

Of course, it begs the question as to why premiums keep growing faster than inflation, and we cover that extensively in this book. But let me give you a sampling of the problem here.

Newtown is served by a hospital located in the neighboring city of Danbury. That hospital, in fact, basically controls the volume and price of medical care for the entire area, extending a couple of dozen miles on either side. And that's typical of many towns in America.

For a couple of years I served on the finance committee of the hospital, a voluntary position that advises the hospital

Board on a variety of issues related to the hospital's finances. At one of the committee's meetings, a hospital official related the recent "success" of negotiations with the largest health plans. And pretty much everyone marveled at the numbers. The hospital had been able to get price increases between 15% and 20% with the different insurers. One of the committee members congratulated the hospital official for "socking it to the health plans." At which point I reminded them that it wasn't the health plans they were socking it to, it was every resident in each community the hospital served. Because the health plans don't absorb these price increases, they simply raise insurance premiums. And everyone that pays those premiums pays for the hospital's price increases.

What struck me most was the complete disconnect for those governing the hospital between the actions of the hospital and the direct consequences on the communities they are supposed to serve. They simply jacked up their prices because they could. They basically have a monopoly in their market, and the plans have to accept the increases. At no point in the two years I served was there ever a conversation about significantly changing the way health care was delivered to improve the value of premium dollars spent, or of truly maximizing efficiencies within existing plant and equipment. The normal business conversation that occurs everyday in every other sector of the economy is almost completely absent from health care organizations. The only concern they seem to have is how to raise prices, not how to reduce expenses. And since, in most cases, they can get away with it, they have.

Today the impact is clear. Municipal budgets, including school budgets, can no longer go up, and the rise in health care premiums has to be offset, usually by layoffs. We've collectively become impoverished by a massive transfer of our wealth to a single economic sector that has grown, not because it delivers incredible value and is capturing markets overseas, but because the warped incentives have made it an insatiable ogre. And we're the gruel off of which it feeds.

Incomes – After more than two decades of health care costs growing much faster than the rest of the economy, we're surely approaching the breaking point. Today, our debt is larger than ever. Our kids and grandkids will be saddled with the interest payments for decades to come, and unless we reduce spending *and* raise tax revenue, their burdens will only grow heavier. Of course, it's not just the government feeling the pain. *Increases in care costs have also had a huge negative impact on the private sector, especially on the average family.* Overall, average household income is 10% less than what it should be, because the wages employees should have brought home were instead used to cover the fast rising costs of health care premiums.10 It's a key reason why real household income (as measured in inflation-adjusted dollars) has barely budged since 2000.

Figure 3: Average Household Income Lost To Health Insurance Premiums

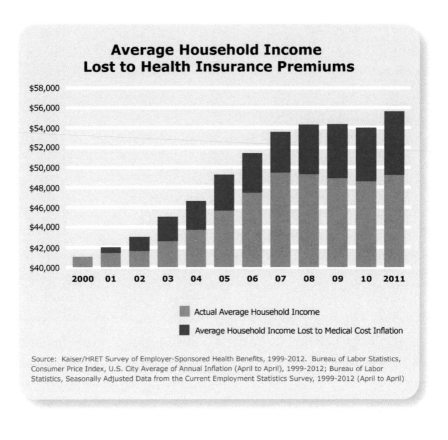

Average Household Income Lost to Health Insurance Premiums

Legend:
- Actual Average Household Income
- Average Household Income Lost to Medical Cost Inflation

Source: Kaiser/HRET Survey of Employer-Sponsored Health Benefits, 1999-2012. Bureau of Labor Statistics, Consumer Price Index, U.S. City Average of Annual Inflation (April to April), 1999-2012; Bureau of Labor Statistics, Seasonally Adjusted Data from the Current Employment Statistics Survey, 1999-2012 (April to April)

Figure 3 – The True Reason For Stagnant Incomes

Since 2000, the average household income, unadjusted for inflation, has gone up by $8,000 – from about $41,200 to 49,200. That's an increase of about 20%, or slightly less than 2% per year. Unfortunately, the price of food, gas, utilities, homes, and most everything else, including health care, has also increased every year, and by slightly more than 2%. As a result, adjusted for inflation, household income has actually gone down by about 10%. In other words, households today buy less with their take home pay than they did a decade ago.

While the price of food, gas and other goods and services did increase, what really hammered households is the significantly greater increase in the costs of health care. In fact, the total cost of insuring a family has gone up by close to 40%, twice as fast as anything else in the economy. If health insurance premium costs had simply risen at the same level as all other costs, the yearly price for a family would be $8,400 instead of $15,000 – a difference of $6,600.

And, during these past ten years, if employers who provide health insurance had given that difference to employees, then household income would be close to $56,000 today instead of $49,000. As such, adjusted for inflation, household income would have gone up since 2000 rather than going down. That's the real reason for stagnant incomes.

You see, typically in a recession wages don't go up by much, but neither do prices, because people consume less and save a little more. Unfortunately, health care prices continued to rise way more than inflation, simply because "someone else" is paying for it, and the normal market forces that kept prices down in other sectors of the economy didn't come into play in this one.

In this book you'll discover the reasons why health care costs keep going up, and the recipes to reverse this trend. We've already paid a heavy price for this runaway inflation, and it has to stop.

So we pay more per person than anyone else, we have average health outcomes, prices have spiraled out of control and led to higher insurance premiums, and the average American family is all the poorer for it. Aren't we getting anything for all these extra dollars being spent?

Is it all bad? *specialized medicine

In fairness, we do rank highly in some areas. In a comparison of five countries, the Commonwealth Fund reported that the U.S. had the best survival rate for breast cancer, and tied for the best survival rate for colorectal cancer.7 The U.S. also ranked first in providing the "right care" for a given condition based on standard clinical guidelines, and earned high marks for preventive screenings like pap smears and mammograms to detect early-stage cancers, and blood tests and cholesterol checks for patients with hypertension.

In other bright spots, Americans can typically see a specialist more quickly than most citizens abroad, and we have done a better job than other industrialized nations in reducing smoking rates. Physicians and hospitals also have access to more and newer high-end tools than most any other country in the world. For example, some surgical centers have sophisticated robots to assist in complex surgeries; a physician in a medical center on one coast can guide a physician in another medical center on the other coast to perform a procedure or consult a patient; organs are routinely transplanted in young and old patients; and new medical implants that transform patient lives are developed and tested every day.

And there's another hopeful note: *Newly enacted health reform legislation in the U.S. will start to address many of the problems that have led to the mediocre ratings we've discussed in this chapter.* The Patient Protection and Affordable Care Act, known by supporters and detractors alike as Obamacare, is a long way from

- cadillac tax
- individual mandate

perfect, but it does contain many provisions designed to attack current cost and quality problems. *x now its been stripped*

So it certainly is not all bad. In some instances, what we get is really good. But in many instances, what we pay for has no value whatsoever. How do we tell the difference? In many cases we can't, and that's a huge problem. And since we pay for most everything indiscriminately, we get what we pay for…good and bad. And that has to change for everything to improve.

In some ways, we are the problem and the problem is us

If a student with no parental support shows up for school every day tired and ill-prepared, pays no attention in class, never does the homework, and, as a result, scores poorly on standardized tests, is that the teachers' fault? Can you really lay all the blame on the school system rather than the parents, or the community, or the student?

In defending the U.S. health care system, some analysts make an argument along similar lines. And they have a point. For example, plenty of Americans have terrible dietary and exercise habits, which have led to a dramatic increase in obesity rates over the past 20 years. According to the Centers for Disease Control 2009-2010 National Health and Nutrition Examination Survey, more than one-third of U.S. adults and approximately 17% of children and adolescents aged 2-19 are obese.[11, 12] The medical care costs are staggering. In 2008, they totaled about $147 billion.[13]

This brings us to two negative incentives that began with the best of intentions, but ended up having harmful effects.

First, linking health insurance to employment has led employers to offer rich and ever-expanding benefits to attract and keep the best and brightest workers. ***For generations, this has insulated the*** *what would it look like to be truly "informed"?*

actual consumer of health care services – the patient – from the total costs of those services. So unlike other forms of insurance, no transparent market could develop around health care services. Consumers had no incentive to become informed active buyers, as they have with other expensive products and services, because the big financial decisions were essentially taken out of their hands. The employee typically paid just a small share of the actual cost of services. As a result, insurers and providers had no incentive to make those costs transparent, or to subject them to the normal rules of supply and demand.

As employees got used to this "third-party payer" system, they viewed any attempt to increase their share of the costs as an attack on their cherished benefits. It's hard to blame them. But this disconnect between sellers and buyers of health care services formed the root of the "anything goes" and "submit your bill and we'll pay" way of doing business that has served the U.S. so poorly.

As a way to combat this, there has been a sharp rise in the number of companies offering only high-deductible/high co-insurance health plans – also known as "consumer-directed" plans – in which workers pay a higher share of the costs up to a certain defined amount. In the short term, this is not necessarily a win for consumers, since they have to pay more out of their own pockets until their insurance benefits kick in. Long term, however, the evidence is pretty clear that these plans work a lot better at turning the average consumer of health care services into a more active purchaser; and that can go a long way toward reducing overall costs of care across the system.[14] These plans need further refinements, and these consumer-patients need better information (more on that later), but they're finally moving us back into a zone that resembles more typical consumer purchasing behavior.

Employment-based Health Insurance: A Fluke of History

Earlier in the century, there was no systematic approach to either health care or health insurance. If you got sick, you went to the doctor or the doctor came to you. Fees were modest, and the average family spent very little on health care. In addition, many doctors were poorly trained, and treatments often primitive. With trusted information scarce, many people had a hard time telling the difference between actual medicine and utter quackery. And so we had the likes of Dr. John Brinkley, who grew fantastically rich implanting goat testicles in men as a cure for pretty much anything that might be ailing them, especially their waning virility. As Brinkley reasoned in his popular radio programs, did you ever see a billy goat that was anything but extremely frisky?

The modern idea of health insurance didn't even exist until about 1930, when one Texas hospital began offering local teachers a deal: Give us 50 cents a month and if you get sick, we'll provide medical services for no extra charge. Thus, for a small fee, a group of workers gained financial protection against the risk of serious illness. The hospital, in turn, gained a steady steam of income to help cover expenses during the Great Depression. A beneficial arrangement for both parties, the concept spread quickly to other hospitals in other states, creating the framework of what came to be known as Blue Cross.[15]

During the forties and fifties, many companies expanded on the idea by offering their employees health insurance. Congress encouraged this practice by treating employer contributions to worker health benefits as a tax-deductible business expense. As a result, this quickly became the primary way most Americans obtained health insurance. For several generations of workers, who tended to stay put in their jobs for decades, it worked pretty well.

But it's a pretty strange notion when you think about it. Why should your health insurance be connected to your job? We don't get our life, home, or auto insurance through work. We make our own buying decisions in competitive markets, based on cost and coverage information that's easy to understand and compare. Why should health insurance be so different? Further, why should companies be responsible for providing health insurance to their workers, especially now that people change jobs so frequently? In a global economy, these costs (for both current employees and retirees) often put American companies at an automatic disadvantage when competing with foreign companies that don't have to bear that burden – $11,429 per covered family in 2012.

Second, for years, the Farm Bill – subsidies begun to help farmers survive the Great Depression – has supported the production of commodity crops such as corn, wheat, soy, rice, and cotton. These are the crops that make up high fructose corn syrup and hydrogenated oils, and are used to fatten up grain-fed beef cattle. *As such, the government has provided incentives for farmers to grow the crops that make calorie-laden fast food and junk food so cheap and pervasive.* Healthier agricultural products such as fresh food and vegetables receive much lower federal subsidies, which is partly why healthier food is so expensive. The bottom line is that foods very high in calories and fat are much more affordable to people on tight food budgets, and Americans today consume more than 20% more calories a day than we did in the early 1980s.[16]

But none of this is the fault of the health care industry. Higher-calorie junk foods lead directly to higher obesity rates, which lead directly to higher chronic disease rates, which lead directly to higher care costs for all of us, because most of the time it's "someone else's money." The point is that our health care system doesn't exist apart from society. Rather, it simply reflects society. The choices we make as a people – our laws, our habits, our priorities – all have an impact on health care. In many ways, we are the problem, and the problem is us.

Let's face it, in other countries far poorer than the U.S., or where income per family is much lower, health care systems deliver more value. For example, infant mortality is lower in many countries because certain best practices are simply mandated as a condition of payment. And many other countries have done a much more effective job of promoting active competition among clinicians and facilities for the management of patients. Even India, which has four times the population of the U.S., has launched models of payment that encourage competition among providers and keep health care inflation in check while increasing quality.[17] And that country is widely known for being a bureaucratic nightmare. As a result, some U.S. employers have even offered to send their employees to get certain procedures done in India.[18, 19]

Perhaps we've tolerated our higher-cost, lower-performing system because, until recently, we've seemingly been able to afford it. But in the wake of the Great Recession, deficits have ballooned, wages have stagnated, and we all must realize we can no longer tolerate this fiasco. Do we really believe that doctors and hospitals in this country can't offer better value than their colleagues in India? Do we really need to outsource our health care? Are we really incapable of doing better?

Of course not. Americans used to do big things together. We squared our shoulders and met our challenges. Now it's time to mobilize for a new national project: Fixing our health care system once and for all. We believe the only way to do this is one patient, one provider, one decision at a time. Yes, it's complicated, but far from impossible. The Affordable Care Act holds the promise of much needed change and discipline. But it's not enough; we cannot and should not rely on the government to provide all the solutions. Every health care consumer, purchaser, and provider has a critical role to play if we are to succeed. Later, we'll describe the pressure points each of us can apply to accelerate positive change. Because in the end, we are also the solution – only we can apply the needed cure.

It starts by understanding exactly how the health care industry manages to waste $750 billion a year. The picture is not pretty.

Chapter 2 – Wasteland

Poor management of patients. Hospital readmissions. Patient safety failures. Too many tests and procedures. Bloated bureaucracy. Avoidable complications. Patients who don't take their meds. Plain old fraud. These are the kinds of issues that cause nearly a third of our total health care spending to go up in smoke. By reducing this level of waste, we could probably freeze spending at current levels for well over a decade without affecting care quality or access at all. But doing so will require major changes in our collective attitudes about health care – not just in how it's delivered, but also in how it's consumed. Let's look at some of the most serious forms of waste, and specific ways in which we can administer a cure.

The Institute of Medicine's Reports On The Quality Of Health Care in America.

In late 1999, the Institute of Medicine (IOM) published the first of a series of reports on the quality of health care in the United States. IOM is an independent, nonprofit organization that works outside of government to provide unbiased and authoritative advice to decision makers and the public. Established in 1970, the IOM is the health arm of the National Academy of Sciences, which was chartered under President Abraham Lincoln in 1863. Nearly 150 years later, the National Academy of Sciences has expanded into what is collectively known as the National Academies, which comprise the National Academy of Sciences, the National Academy of Engineering, the National Research Council, and the IOM.

In the first report, entitled *To Err is Human: Building A Safer Health System*, the IOM reported that between 50,000 and 100,000 people die every year from preventable errors.[20] While more than a decade later the statistics haven't changed much, the report did launch a series of national efforts that have led to public reporting of certain quality of care measures, and a change in the way Medicare pays hospitals and physicians.

The second report, published in 2001 and entitled *Crossing the Quality Chasm: A New Health System for the 21st Century*, shed light on the importance of payment.[21] The IOM referred to the way most physicians and hospitals are paid as a "toxic payment environment" in which bad behaviors are rewarded and good behaviors are punished.

It also referred to the distance between the level of quality care that should be delivered and the level actually provided, as a chasm – a deep and large gap. That report also launched a series of national demonstration projects by Medicare and private sector organizations to test new models of payment, quality reporting, and improvement in the underlying systems that support clinicians. The results of many of those projects led to the inclusion of significant payment reform and reporting initiatives in the Affordable Care Act.

However, in 2013, the toxic payment environment is still here (we'll discuss the disaster of fee-for-service in the next chapter), the quality chasm is still deep and wide, and many of the solutions laid out by the IOM haven't been implemented. All Americans must get involved to force the solutions through.

Mismanaged patients with chronic conditions

There's no question that chronic conditions are the driver of health care costs, partially because so many Americans have one or more of these conditions, and partially because there is so much mismanagement of these conditions…by patients and providers. And both are mostly driven by bad incentives.

Consider the chart below. It illustrates the average cost of treating a patient with diabetes for one year across six different practices, A through F. These are real physician practices and real costs for real patients that we analyzed as part of a project I did in 2011. All these patients are enrolled in Medicaid, and there are no major differences among them that would explain why the average cost in practice F is $7,000 a year, while the average is about half of that in practice A.

Figure 4: Average Yearly Cost Of Patients With Diabetes, By Practice, And Overall

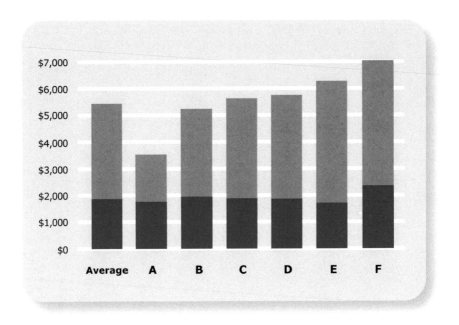

The blue part of the column represents costs for routine care for diabetes, such as visits to the practice, diabetic supplies, and medication. The orange part represents avoidable complications – things like visits to the emergency department (ED) and hospitalizations because of poor management of diabetes. You'll notice that the blue portion doesn't vary much from practice to practice, but the orange portion does. And that's what we find for most chronic conditions, across the country. For some chronic conditions, close to two-thirds of the average costs are consumed by avoidable complications, and for others it can be one-third. Overall, it's a lot. *regional geographic patient adherence*

But if patients in these practices are pretty much the same, why is it that Practice A seems to be doing so much better? What's their secret? Well, it's pretty simple. They actively manage their patients. They follow up regularly to make sure the patients are taking their meds, and are feeling okay. They have an electronic medical record and track the vitals of their patients. *Collaborative care*

The other practices are doing some of that, but not as much, and Practice F is not doing much of it at all. Why is that? Well, for one, Practice A is paid a single global fee to cover all of the costs of diabetes (including an allowance for complications). As a result, whenever Practice A helps a patient avoid an ED visit, they actually benefit financially. Think about it. Doing a good job for the patients is highly rewarded. *BUNDLED PAYMENTS value based ID*

On the other hand, Practice F is paid for every office visit (not much, because typically Medicaid pays little for those visits), and if patients of Practice F go to the ED or end up in the hospital, there are no financial consequences for the practice. In fact, to an extent, Practice F would likely lose money if they deployed a lot of time and resources managing their diabetics (see Camden story below). And so it goes, everywhere, for pretty much every area of care.

This example helps to show why fee-for-service payment is so harmful. Under fee-for-service, providers are compensated based on how many services they deliver, not on the overall quality of their care. There's no incentive to coordinate care and reach out to patients who need support, which are the keys to the success of Practice A. In fact, they have every financial incentive to *avoid* working in this way, even though it's absolutely the best way to improve and maintain patient health (much more on this in Chapter 3.)

Avoidable hospital readmissions

These are readmissions that occur after a patient leaves the hospital, perhaps due to issues like wound infections, a botched procedure, poor coordination of care, or even retained surgical items like surgical sponges left in the patient's body. Of course, it could also be because some of the patients failed to properly take care of themselves.

The Agency for Healthcare Research and Quality (AHRQ) says nearly 20% of Medicare hospitalizations are followed by readmission within 30 days.[22] According to the Medicare Payment Advisory Commission (MedPAC), 75% of readmissions are preventable. To address this problem, the Affordable Care Act restricts Medicare payments for hospital readmissions that occur within 30 days, and prohibits payments for provider errors.[23] That's a good start – an avoidable readmission should not be a revenue opportunity – but not enough.

Why do readmissions happen so often? Because it's really tough to always do the right thing when you're financially penalized for it.

Consider the Community Asthma Initiative at Children's Hospital in Boston. It adopted a new systematic approach for managing inner-city children who suffer severe asthma attacks. The hospital introduced a series of preventive measures, of which insurance would cover just one: prescribing an inhaler. The hospital agreed to cover the rest. These included nurses who visited parents after discharge to make sure they had their child's medicine, knew how to use it, and had scheduled a follow-up appointment. Other measures included home inspections for mold and pests, and vacuum cleaners to help keep the child's environment as clean as possible (which, it turns out, can be cheaper and more effective than medication). After a year, the hospital readmission rate for these patients dropped by more than 80%, and costs dropped accordingly.[24]

It's a great story, but here's the rub. A program this successful should clearly be a model for other hospitals across the country. But once more, external incentives can get in the way. An empty hospital bed equals lost revenue (much like for a hotel), and asthma is Children's Hospital's leading source of admissions. Under the fee-for-service payment system, this innovative program that greatly improves patient health actually imposes a severe financial penalty on the hospital that created it. *In other words, strictly from a business standpoint, what's good for the patient is bad for the hospital, and vice-versa.*

* * *

The Cure: Readmission rates and other quality outcomes of hospitals are reported and calculated by different organizations and available to the public at no charge. For example, "Why Not the Best?" is supported by the Commonwealth Fund and provides a series of quality measures for all hospitals in the country. In addition, a new site provides a useful patient safety score for a hospital. Use both tools before choosing a hospital, and reward the one in your area that has better outcomes and lower preventable readmissions with your "business." It's only by voting with our feet that we'll start to create the business case for hospitals to continuously improve their performance.

* * *

Managing Chronic Care Patients in Camden, NJ

Camden is a rough city that recently rose to some fame (see Frontline report featuring well-known physician Dr. Atul Gawande) because of the actions of a doctor, Jeff Brenner, who single-handedly showed how the old saying "penny-wise and pound-foolish" applies to health care.[25] After getting his medical degree, Dr. Brenner decided to open a practice in one of the tougher sections of Camden. There, most patients were covered by Medicaid, many lived at or under the federal poverty level, and a significant number suffered from chronic disease. Medicaid in NJ, like in most states, is always trying to find ways to get more value for the dollars spent, and yet they seem to have gone at it all wrong. Their penny-wise approach has been to cut the reimbursement rates for physicians like Dr. Brenner who were trying to manage their patients' chronic conditions. And by cutting these rates, Dr. Brenner didn't make enough on each patient visit to cover the rent of his practice or staff salaries. As a result, he closed his practice, forced to leave his patients to seek care elsewhere. The elsewhere, as it turns out, was the hospital.

Dr. Brenner then started to figure out why Medicaid costs were continuing to go up while they kept slashing the reimbursement rates for physician services. And he found a few startling facts:

- Medicaid was spending hundreds of millions in hospital care for patients who should get their care in physician offices instead. The lack of physician care in community practices led the patients to be hospitalized, with each hospitalization costing 20 to 30 times more than the physician office visit.

- Some patients were "frequent flyers," ending up in the hospital 10 or more times a year...some every week.

- Most of these patients lived in one of two public housing buildings with no community-based physicians nearby.

So in collaboration with Medicaid and others in the city, he launched a project to deliver focused care management to these "frequent flyers" – high utilizers as Dr. Brenner refers to them. The results were dramatic. Hospitalizations decreased to zero in some instances, and hundreds of thousands of dollars were saved.

Avoidable or preventable hospitalizations for patients with chronic illness are just that – they don't have to happen. Good management of those patients by community-based physicians can and does eliminate hospital stays, and results in far higher quality care for the patients. But to take full advantage, payers like Medicaid must stop being penny-wise and pound-foolish.

Patient safety failures   *hand washing

This is an area in which it's very hard to find hard numbers, and here's why. We sometimes read about the most dramatic failures (like a wrong limb being amputated), but for every one of these, hundreds more are never reported. Although a national voluntary reporting effort was launched to gather these patient safety failures, few hospitals are volunteering the information, and right now they don't have to. There is really no formal organization or mandated process to help reduce cases like the one at NYU Langone Medical Center, in which a 12-year-old boy died after being sent home with a much more serious infection than his doctors recognized.[26]

Think about this for a moment. If a nurse or clinical aide gets hurt while moving a patient, or suffers a concussion after slipping on a wet floor, that event must be reported to the Occupational Safety and Health Administration (OSHA) because it involves workplace safety. But if a patient is grievously injured or even killed in the same facility, there's no official investigation, no mandatory reporting, just higher health care expenses. How does this make sense? *If OSHA inspectors can investigate a workplace injury in a hospital, why can't the Department of Health and Human Services send an equivalent task force to investigate a patient's accidental death?* Taking the comparison even further, if public health officials can inspect and rate restaurants, why can't they inspect and rate hospitals? Why do we tolerate this double standard? If you care about your loved ones, you won't. History shows that codes of silence are broken only when enough good people stand up for what's right.

Increasing hospital safety doesn't have to be complicated. For example, AHRQ funded a study that identified a series of simple steps doctors should take to avoid infection when putting IVs into major blood vessels—like putting on a fresh gown, gloves, and mask, and cleansing the skin with a special antiseptic soap. After these became standard practices, infections in intensive care units dropped 58% from 2001 to 2009.[27] In one year alone, the change saved an estimated 6,000 lives and $414 million.[27]

Here again, things are moving – slowly – in a positive direction. The federal government has taken steps to set up a formal consumer reporting system that would allow patients to report medical mistakes and unsafe practices by doctors, hospitals, pharmacists, and other providers. Patients could describe the details of the event, the type of harm it caused, the contributing factors, and more. In addition, more recently, the Leapfrog Group has launched a website that creates a single score for hospitals. But does it go far enough? No.

* * *

The Cure: We need to make national reporting of patient safety failures mandatory for all acute and long-term care facilities that accept Medicare or Medicaid patients. In addition, the Department of Health and Human Services should create a new department, like OSHA, to investigate serious patient safety failures and work with hospitals to institute permanent process changes. Talk to your Senators and Congressional Representatives about sponsoring legislation that would make this a reality. And use the information on www.hospitalsafetyscore.org to start a campaign for better patient safety in your area by publishing each hospital's safety rating in the local papers.

* * *

The testing conundrum

Physicians and hospitals across the U.S. know they perform way too many medical tests. The American College of Physicians (ACP), which represents pretty much all of the nation's primary care physicians, knows it. They've introduced guidelines to help doctors better identify when patients should be screened for certain diseases, and named 37 clinical situations in which screening did not promote health, and may actually cause harm.[28]

The American Board of Internal Medicine Foundation knows it. They've launched a program called Choosing Wisely®, and invited various medical societies to name five tests in their respective fields that should be performed less often. For example, the American Society of Clinical Oncology said doctors should cut back on CT and PET scans for early prostate and breast cancers that are not likely to metastasize. That's an important step, because the volume of MRI, CT and PET scans has skyrocketed in recent years, and some patients are being harmed by unnecessary exposure to radiation.[29]

testing is too sensitive & lacks specificity

So the doctors know they test too often. But do patients? It's a tricky area. Let's say you're a 60-year-old male with no symptoms of prostate problems. But you choose to have a PSA test anyway. It shows a high level of prostate-specific antigen, which may (or may not) indicate you have prostate cancer. A biopsy confirms you have a tiny cancerous tumor at a very early stage that has not spread. What do you do?

You can choose to watch and wait. Because prostate cancer tends to grow very slowly, we know that most men with the disease will eventually die of something else. In fact, prostate cancer often presents no serious negative physical effects. If you get frequent tests that confirm the cancer is not growing at a rapid pace, you may never need to do anything else. But of course you want that cancer gone.

So you may choose to treat it. That can mean surgery, or attacking the cancer with radiation pellets, or some other form of treatment. This will probably eliminate the cancer, and bring great relief to you and your loved ones. But it may also cause really bad long-term side effects, like incontinence or impotence, and impose substantial financial costs.

This illustrates a dilemma with large implications for health care costs. Namely, is the treatment sometimes worse than the disease? Further, does testing sometimes cause more problems than it solves? Yes, and yes.

We know, for example, that more than half of women who get annual mammograms over a ten-year span will receive at least one false positive result.[30] So for every life saved by a mammogram, many more women who don't have cancer will be called back for additional, often invasive tests they don't actually need. Perhaps the mammogram reveals a shadow. That quickly leads to a more comprehensive 3D scan. That scan reveals a mass, which may just be muscle mass. But to play it safe, the doctor performs an immediate biopsy and sends the tissue sample to the lab. And so what started as a routine screening turns into a several-thousand-dollar visit. Was it necessary?

In some cases, yes. In many cases, no. This is really the grey zone of medicine, the area where the clinicians have tremendous discretion, and no one is likely to challenge the decision. And as patients, we want them to use that discretion. However, as a society, we need that discretion to be fully informed by expert opinion rather than by revenue opportunities. The Affordable Care Act includes money for comparative effectiveness studies, which can give guidance on the tests and treatments that are better at saving lives than others. For example, some screenings – such as prostate screening for men who don't have any symptoms – are no longer among the recommended screenings approved by the US Preventive Services Task Force.

There's no simple answer. Certainly, patients need to be better informed about the pros and cons of tests, and understand how they can often prompt great anxiety, more tests, expensive consultations, and unnecessary procedures. *volume ≠ quality*

But a key point to remember is this: *As long as providers are paid for each and every service and test they perform, the incentives are always to treat more rather than less.* So while doctors and nurses might want to do the right thing – which oftentimes is simply watchful waiting – the incentive to do more billable work can be overwhelming. We have only begun to take our first baby steps toward changing the reimbursement system to remove the financial incentives for doctors to provide more tests and treatments. We'll review the details in the next chapter. But patients need to do their part too. Sometimes it's just a matter of asking questions: Why do I need this test? What are the potential benefits? What are the drawbacks? Ask away. You might be surprised at the answers.

* * *

The Cure: The Informed Medical Decisions Foundation has many resources for patients to help you understand the tradeoffs and the evidence for many common procedures. Visit the website and use the resources before seeing your doctor. There are also many resources on the site for physicians, so encourage your doctor to visit the site as well. You have to get involved in the decision-making process and know that more isn't always better.

* * *

The belief that more equals better

Economists from Dartmouth College found that the more money Medicare spent per person in a given state, the lower that state's quality ranking tended to be. In fact, the four states with the highest levels of spending—Louisiana, Texas, California, and Florida—were near the bottom of the national rankings on the quality of patient care.[31]

Another Dartmouth team examined the treatment received by a million elderly Americans diagnosed with colon or rectal cancer, a hip fracture, or a heart attack. Patients in higher-spending regions received 60% more care than elsewhere – more frequent tests and procedures, more visits with specialists, more frequent admission to hospitals.[32] Yet in terms of survival, their ability to function, or their satisfaction with the care they received, they did no better than other patients. If anything, they seemed to do worse.

And here's another example, in Sweden you can get a total knee replacement for $8,500 – including a five year warranty – while in the US, the same procedure costs close to $26,000 for members of commercial health plans, and $22,600 for Medicare.[33] Is the costlier procedure better than the others? No. It's just that hospitals, medical device manufacturers and surgeons can charge health plans a lot more for the exact same procedure.

Figure 5: Average Cost of Knee Replacement Surgery For Medicare, US Commercially Insured, and Sweden

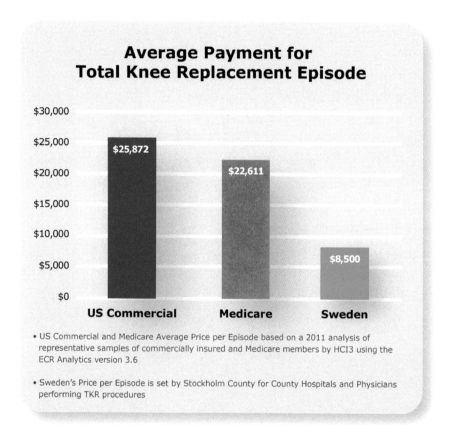

So the next time someone in health care tells you that better health care quality costs more, watch your wallet because it's about to get picked.

Extreme entrepreneurship

In California, a creative group of surgeons decided to invest in building their own orthopedic surgical centers. And they're not accepting insurance. Yet they're making money hand over fist. Why? Because they offer all types of bells and whistles to patients, and the word has gone out. But wait, there's more. Health plan members often get coverage even when they see "out-of-network" physicians. Typically the health plan will apply a deductible, which the doctor is supposed to collect, and pay 80% of the claim, with the balance paid by the patient.

So here's where the "extreme" kicks in. The physicians are billing the health plan 200% to 300% of the normal cost for the surgery. For example, a total knee replacement typically costs $27,000. These entrepreneurs are charging the insurance company $60,000.[34] As mentioned above, the insurance company won't pay the deductible (let's assume it's $1,000) but does pay 80% of the balance. That comes out to a whopping $47,200 or more than twice the average normal cost. As a result, the docs never even ask for the deductible or the co-insurance normally paid by the patient; they're pretty happy with twice what they would otherwise get. We get what we pay for, and in this instance the health plans are paying to get royally screwed.

Without question, entrepreneurship has also created many benefits for the health care system, and plenty of remarkable innovations. *So the solution lies in encouraging the right type of entrepreneurship, focused mainly on new care techniques that benefit the patient and drive the system to greater affordability for all.* Here again patients have a role to play. Always ask your physicians about all the treatment alternatives available to you, and their associated costs. One MRI facility in your area may be far cheaper than others, and provide the same quality. You might get much better value at the pharmacy down the street than the one in the doctor's office. Let's face it, you have every right to know what you're paying before you get the bill.

And it's worth asking: Whose behavior is worse? The perpetrators of these "excesses," or the ones who allow the extreme entrepreneurs to prosper? If we continue to allow abuse on this scale, we have no one to blame but ourselves for our wasteful health care system. If you see evidence of Medicare fraud, report it at www.stopmedicarefraud.gov or call the Department of Health and Human Services at 800-HHS-TIPS (1-800-447-8477). For other types of fraud, report it the Attorney General's office in your state.

Legislatively, these issues can also be addressed with relatively simple measures. First, we can expand the current law that stops physicians from referring patients for tests to facilities in which they own a financial interest. Second, we can demand full price transparency at the point of need for all treatments. This kind of pricing information is slowly becoming more accessible, but there's still a long way to go.

* * *

The Cure: Demand complete transparency in the financial relationships between the physicians and facilities that treat you. Does your doctor own a financial interest in the local diagnostic imaging center? Is the physician paid by the hospital? Does the physician own a patent on a medical device or implant? Is the physician often invited for "educational seminars" to resorts, sponsored by pharmaceutical or medical device manufacturers? All this stuff is going on now, and has been proven to influence physician decision-making. In addition, talk to your federal legislators about extending the anti-kickback statutes to prevent outside financial influence in the clinicians' decision-making.

* * *

Rogues Gallery – Or What Happens When We Encourage People To Be Bad

September 2012 – HCA Inc., one of the nation's largest for-profit hospital chains, agrees to pay the United States and the state of Tennessee $16.5 million to settle claims that it violated the False Claims Act and the Stark Statute. As alleged in the settlement agreement, during 2007, HCA, through its subsidiaries Parkridge Medical Center and HCA Physician Services, entered into a series of financial transactions with a physician group, Diagnostic Associates of Chattanooga, through which it provided financial benefits intended to induce the physician members of Diagnostic to refer patients to HCA facilities. These financial transactions included rental payments for office space leased from Diagnostic at a rate well in excess of fair market value. This isn't the first time HCA makes headlines. In 2003, HCA settled what was then the largest fraud case ever, in which it agreed to pay the United States $631 million in civil penalties and damages arising from false claims the government alleged it submitted to Medicare and other federal health programs. Previously, on December 14, 2000, HCA subsidiaries pled guilty to substantial criminal conduct and paid more than $840 million in criminal fines, civil restitution and penalties. Combined with a separate administrative settlement in 2003 with the Centers for Medicare & Medicaid Services (CMS), under which HCA paid an additional $250 million to resolve overpayment claims arising from certain of its cost reporting practices, the government will have recovered $1.7 billion from HCA.

July 2012 – GlaxoSmithKline, a prescription drug manufacturer, agrees to a $3 billion fine and pleads guilty to promoting two popular drugs for unapproved uses, and to failing to disclose important safety information on a third. Prosecutors said GlaxoSmithKline illegally promoted the drug Paxil for treating depression in children from April 1998 to August 2003, even though the FDA never approved it for anyone under age 18. The corporation also promoted the drug Wellbutrin from January 1999 to December 2003 for weight loss, the treatment of sexual dysfunction, substance addictions and attention deficit hyperactivity disorder, although it was only approved for treatment of major depressive disorder.

May 2012 – More than 100 people are charged and an estimated $450 million in false billings uncovered by federal agents in a nationwide operation. Fifty nine defendants are charged in Miami, seven in Baton Rouge, nine in Houston, eight in Los Angeles, 22 in Detroit, and one each in Chicago and Tampa. Authorities pointed to an alleged scheme involving community mental health centers in Baton Rouge as the largest and among the most egregious. The alleged operation involved recruiting beneficiaries from nursing homes and homeless shelters – some of whom were drug addicted or mentally ill – and providing them with no services or with medically inappropriate services.

February 2012 – Dr. Jacques Roy, a Texas physician, is accused of cheating Medicare and Medicaid out of nearly $380 million between January 2006 and November 2011. Dr. Roy's company is alleged to have certified more Medicare beneficiaries for home health services, and had more beneficiaries under its care, than any other medical practice in the country.

January 2012 – Sandra Jimenez, from Miami, admits to participating in a fraud scheme orchestrated by the owners and operators of American Therapeutic Corporation (ATC);

its management company, Medlink Professional Management Group Inc.; and the American Sleep Institute (ASI). ATC, Medlink and ASI were all Florida corporations headquartered in Miami. ATC ran purported partial hospitalization programs (PHPs) – a form of intensive treatment for severe mental illness – in seven different Florida locations to provide diagnostic sleep disorder testing. All told, these organizations billed $200 million in fraudulent claims to Medicare.

September 2010 – CBS News reports in 60 Minutes the extent of Medicare fraud, in particular in Florida. Watch the episode.

September 2009 – Pfizer, a pharmaceutical company, agrees to pay a $2 billion fine. The case against Pfizer and its subsidiary Pharmacia & Upjohn (Pharmacia) primarily involved so-called off-brand promotion of several drugs, notably the anti-inflammatory drug Bextra. The company promoted the sale of Bextra for uses and at dosages the Food and Drug Administration (FDA) specifically declined to approve for safety reasons. The company agreed to plead guilty to misbranding Bextra—which was pulled from the market in 2005—with the intent to defraud or mislead, and paid a fine of $1.195 billion. Pfizer also agreed to pay an additional $1 billion to resolve allegations under the False Claims Act that it illegally promoted Bextra and three other drugs and paid kickbacks to health care providers to encourage them to prescribe the medication.

Brutal bureaucracy

Even when people disagree on the exact figures (and they do), it's clear that the U.S. has by far the most bureaucratic health care system in the developed world. According to a 2003 study, administration consumes 31% of health care expenditures in the United States, versus 16.7% in Canada.[35] This level of administration certainly keeps a lot of people employed, but it also forces physicians and hospitals to waste endless hours on activities that have no clinical purpose. And it forces patients to pay much more for services across the board.

In the U.S., hospitals and physicians must deal with dozens of private insurance companies that have negotiated different rates for their members, as well as individuals who have to be billed directly for care not covered by insurance, and other issues that cause them to incur huge overhead expenses. The result is, simply, chaos. *In one hospital, ten different patients can have the exact same surgery and receive the exact same medication and services. But depending on whether those patients have insurance, and what fees those insurers have negotiated, the hospital will receive ten different reimbursement amounts.* These amounts are only partially based on what those services actually cost, and often bear little relation to any objective market reality.

As a result, every hospital has an enormous billing department. Every practice devotes significant resources to paperwork, letting some patients in, keeping other patients out, figuring out which insurer negotiated which rate for which service. And a veritable army of pharmacy benefit managers, imaging benefit managers, physical therapy benefit managers and others earn healthy service fees trying to make sense of it all. Who pays the price for all this bureaucracy? You and me.

The sad and frustrating point is that there are many common sense steps we can take to cut the red tape now.

[handwritten annotation: a huge cost of medical systems to transition (EPIC) to EMRs]

- *First,* we suggest that payers and providers electronically exchange eligibility, claims, and other administrative information on all patients as soon as possible.
- *Second,* providers and payers, including Medicare and Medicaid, should use a single, standardized physician credentialing system. (Currently, physicians must submit their credentials to multiple payers and hospitals.)
- *Third,* payers should provide monthly explanation of benefits statements electronically but allow patients to opt for paper statements.
- *Fourth,* electronic health records should integrate clinical and administrative functions — such as billing, prior authorization, and payments — over the next five years. For instance, ordering a clinical service for a patient could automatically bill the payer in one step. Almost every other industry has figured out how to digitize these functions. It's time health care did as well.
- *Fifth,* we recommend that a task force consisting of payers, providers, and vendors set binding compliance targets, monitor use rates, and have broad authority to implement additional measures that will bring administrative spending in line with other nations.

Docs on defense

For all this talk of waste and corruption and lack of adequate care, it's also important to state this clearly: Among the ranks of physicians, the heroes far outnumber the villains. Doctors genuinely want to help people. That's central to their being; everything else is secondary, and thank goodness for that. *But there is no question that the current system often creates situations in which there are structural impediments to doing the right things for patients.*

Clinicians are encouraged to produce services to boost their income, and to potentially defend against lawsuits. While we can argue about the true impact of "defensive medicine" – when doctors take measures designed primarily to safeguard against malpractice liability, rather than to ensure the health of the patient – there's no doubt that it simply reinforces the basic incentive of fee-for-service to always do more.

Let's face it, clinicians have only one resource – their time. And it's finite. How they use that time during the day will determine their revenue, as will the amount of money they receive for the time spent on patient care. For that matter, many doctors, especially primary care physicians, feel they used to be reimbursed more fairly for their services. And they're right. As reimbursement rates for them have stagnated, or even declined in real terms, they've responded by simply increasing the quantity of services they provide –reducing time spent with each patient to increase the number of visits and services per day. After all, the cost of living isn't going down for anybody. (The next chapter will explain why primary care payments have decreased while other fees have increased.) average = 12 mins

In a sense, defensive medicine provides a handy cover to explain the overuse of tests and procedures. The threat of malpractice is certainly real, and many physicians fear they'll be sued if they fail to offer that extra test and miss something important that harms a patient's health. And it does have an impact – in one anonymous survey cited by (Dr. Sanjay Gupta) in a widely circulated op-ed, orthopedic surgeons said 24% of the tests they ordered were medically unnecessary, and done mostly to protect the doctor or hospital against potential lawsuits.[36] This guy has been on Dr. Oz a tou.

Still, given the overall scope of wasteful spending, it's far from the largest problem. A 2010 study estimates that overall medical No liability system costs, including defensive medicine, were about thanks. 2.4% ($55.6 billion) of total national health care spending in 2008.[37]

A promising strategy to address this important issue would provide a so-called "safe harbor." With it, physicians would be presumed to have done their best if they used qualified health information technology systems and adhered to independently defined, objective, evidence-based clinical practice guidelines.[38] If they wanted, physicians could use clinical-decision support systems to make sure they're working within these guidelines. This way, they could use the safe harbor as an affirmative defense at an early stage of litigation, and introduce evidence to avoid a courtroom battle of the experts. The patient could still present evidence that the guidelines were not applicable to a particular situation, and the judge and jury would, of course, have the final say.

"evidence-based" is extremely hard to change or update. Funding for research is backed by

The way forward *American corporations(i.e. Nestle, Coke, etc*

As we have seen, our health care system is like a giant bucket with a hundred little holes in the bottom. We fill the bucket with our premiums, deductibles, co-pays and coinsurance, but the rampant waste just prevents the bucket from ever filling up, and that money from ever being used to cover only appropriate services. But some great organizations are attacking the problem directly and pointing the way forward.

Some of the best work in identifying and reducing waste is being done in Wisconsin, at ThedaCare, and from there, spreading to other health systems in the country. ThedaCare, the largest healthcare provider in Northeast Wisconsin, says they "searched the globe to discover how to create better systems and eliminate unnecessary steps." For example, they introduced standardized processes for emergency heart attack and stroke treatment that dramatically reduce the time it takes to receive life-saving treatment. They improved productivity in their Radiation Department by 30%, which allows radiation staff to spend more time on patient care.[39]

They reduced the wait time for alcohol and drug treatment by 75%, which increases the chance that needed treatment will begin. And they cut the time it takes to complete admissions paperwork in half. Thanks to these kinds of efforts, ThedaCare has had the lowest price increases in all of northeastern Wisconsin hospitals since 2004 and continue to be the lowest in that state.[40] Systems like ThedaCare show that we could likely freeze spending at current levels for well over a decade and there would still plenty of money to cover all needed services for all Americans.

But really, we all need to take it personally.

James Dichter of Massachusetts did. He saw his insurance company was charged $83 for an arm sling, and found a comparable one online for just $7. After complaining to government agencies and his insurance company, Dichter got his charge forgiven, and highlighted how inflated costs are often simply passed through the health care system.

Robert Burleigh of Virginia did. He saw an overcharge on his emergency room bill, documented the issue carefully, and got that bill reduced. More importantly, he brought scrutiny to the way electronic health systems sometimes show charges for services never performed.

Doris Ace of Texas did. The 82-year-old grandmother joined an undercover media sting to expose Medicare fraud. Ace helped us see exactly how crooks use phony diagnoses to bill for services, supplies and equipment patients neither need nor use.

Brave fighters all in the war against waste. What about you?

However brave we may each be individually, we must act collectively to force through changes in the underlying incentives. As we've said, we're getting what we're paying for today, and we're paying for a lot of unneeded services, a lot of waste, and a lot of hurt. That has to change.

Chapter 3 – It's the Incentives, Stupid!

For decades, perverse payment incentives have distorted the health care delivery system and blocked the kind of change we all know we need. To see why, you need to understand exactly how medical services are paid. For the most part, every time a doctor or facility bills an insurer for a given service, that insurer (whether a government-run program like Medicare or a private company like Blue Cross), pays a negotiated rate for that service. When a medication is prescribed, it's paid for. When a test is ordered, it's paid for. When a patient goes for a simple elective surgery like the repair of a torn ACL, the surgeon's time, of course, is paid. Same for the anesthesiologist if one was present, and each of the materials used, down to the last stitch.

Seems sensible enough. What exactly is the problem? For the answer, you need to pull back the curtain a little. Once you see what's behind it, you'll understand the root cause of the industry's uncontrolled finances – about $8 billion in spending every day, an estimated $2.7 trillion in 2011.[41]

The disaster of fee-for-service

Fee-for-service (FFS) encourages providers to deliver as many medical services as possible. The more you use, the more you bill, the more you get paid. In some instances, that's the right incentive. For example we all want to encourage immunizations for kids, and flu vaccinations for older Americans. Generally, we want to encourage physicians to deliver preventive care, and FFS does the job. However, that incentive is the wrong one when it comes to other care services. As we've seen in the prior chapter, taken to its extreme, FFS pays for readmissions, for patient safety failures, for unneeded tests and surgeries; the "Rogues Gallery" shows to what extent FFS has encouraged bad behaviors. It has turned into FFA – a free-for-all. Except it's not free because we're all paying the bill.

But fee-for-service doesn't just waste money and encourage overtreatment. It also discourages collaboration among physicians or strong proactive management of patients. In fact, there is actually a strong incentive to avoid collaboration, because not working together enables each doctor to generate more services and therefore more income.[31]

Perhaps you, like untold others, have had this experience. After an injury, your primary care doctor orders a series of tests and sends you on to a specialist. The specialist orders more tests. Later on, you realize the second set of tests included many of the same ones you already had. Why? The two doctors simply have no incentive to coordinate your care, or even communicate with each other. Quite the opposite – they have every financial incentive to work within their individual silos and generate as many paid services as possible. As a result, FFS presents a massive barrier to the formation of care teams that we know provide more integrated and efficient care for patients.

The invisible provider-insurer tug of war

We all know that price negotiations depend a lot on the market power of each side. Walmart, for example, gets a better price from most of its suppliers than a smaller retailer. And a merchant on Amazon who reduces his price might get a lot more business. The common theme is that the consumer benefits from those negotiations, and the seller who keeps prices low, at equal quality, will get more business. Not so in health care.

Hospitals are compensated in different ways. For example, Medicare typically pays hospitals a flat fee for each hospital case, with prices based on something called Diagnosis Related Groups, or DRGs. Essentially, the government sets a price for each procedure, adjusts it for the complexity and severity of the case, and the hospital is paid that amount.[42] While hospitals often complain these rates are too low, the system is at least fairly straightforward. In addition, the DRG rates are published on a government website for everyone to see.

Contrast this with the way private insurers compensate hospitals. Typically, each insurer negotiates with each hospital each year. They hammer out costs for things like per-diem payments (a daily fee for inpatient stays – something like room and board in a very expensive hotel) as well as fees for individual services and supplies. And those negotiated rates are hidden. In fact, some hospitals and physician groups insist that the plans cannot, under any circumstances, disclose those negotiated rates. As you might expect, this often leads to wide variations in the costs of medical services at different hospitals. But it can also lead to wide cost variations for the same services within the same hospital. It's like a restaurant charging vastly different prices for the same meal based on which credit card you use to pay for it.

Why? Because no one sees the prices until after the fact. To extend the analogy, it's as if the restaurant has no prices on the menu, you don't have to pay the check on the way out, and you can't even find out what the whole dinner costs until you get your credit card statement. And that's a big reason why health care is not an efficient market. Third parties negotiate prices that are applied to individuals who have no idea of the costs of what they're buying, so market share can't really be affected by consumer decisions.

In other words, *whether the insurance company or the provider wins the negotiations, the consumer-patient has no way of knowing what health care services really cost. This distorts the overall market, and hurts many more people than it helps, because no one really has an incentive to keep prices low.*

* * *

The Cure: Demand to know the price of services up front, from your health plan and your doctors and hospitals. You have a right to know, especially in a high deductible/high co-insurance plan, and you should never take no for an answer. If your health plan can't tell you how much a common procedure like a knee replacement will cost you, then change plans as soon as you can for one that will answer the question. In addition, some states have enacted legislation that stops health plans and providers to collude by having "gag clauses" in their contracts. Find out what your state is doing and talk to your legislators about fixing this problem.

* Surprise Billing   * * *

The $517 X-Ray, by Dr. Abramson as reported in Costs of Care Blog

So the story goes like this. A patient of mine needed a chest x-ray. He doesn't have health insurance, so rather than just give him a requisition and send him to the local hospital; I decided to do a little calling around on his behalf to find out what the damage would be…

Vendor #1: A well-known local hospital

I called up the radiology department and asked them how much a PA and Lateral Chest X-ray would cost. "I don't know – we don't have that information," I was told by the clerk. The radiologist gave me the same answer. They both said I should just send the patient over and he would find out the cost when he received the bill.

That seemed a little dumb. Since when do we go into stores and buy things without knowing the price? So after 4 additional phone calls and about 2 hours, my assistant and I finally reached Bob who is in charge of uninsured patient billing. He was able to tell me the price: **$517**. For a PA and Lateral Chest x-ray!

For cash paying patients who pay at the time of service and *know to ask for the "20-20" discount* by name, the price ends up being reduced to **$310.20**. But you have to know the secret code word.

Time to receive report in my office: 2-3 days.

Quality: Good

Vendor #2: Free-Standing Private Radiology Office

I called up and the receptionist answered on the first ring. I asked how much for a PA and Lateral Chest x-ray. An immediate answer: **$73**.

Time to receive report in my office: 1 hour.

Quality: Just as Good

So my question is this. How can the hospital be charging 4.25 times as much as the place down the street to cash-paying patients, for the same product and actually inferior response time (or 7 times as much without the secret code word)? I know, "cost shifting" is a common refrain. But that just doesn't fly any more. And what's more disturbing, how can it be so difficult to find out the price when you call up and ask?

Many doctors just send their patients to the hospital x-ray department or lab without thinking that it may bankrupt them. And many doctors have no idea that the price spread can be so great.

Why you can't understand your medical bills

Go ahead, take a look at one of your bills. Wade through that jumble of dates, codes, acronyms, charges, adjustments, quantities, and payments by insurance. See if you can figure out what services you actually received, how much they actually cost, and whether those figures are correct or not.

If there was a mistake, could you even spot it? Medical Billing Advocates of America, a national association that reviews bills for consumers, says 8 of 10 hospital bills it sees contain errors.[43] There are myriad ways a bill can be wrong – incorrect data entry, duplicate orders, fees applied individually instead of in bundles, inflated charges, "upcoding" to a condition that requires more costly care. And on and on and on. Why? Because of the antiquated way in which medical bills are negotiated (a fee for every service) and paid (negotiated service by negotiated service).

For example, every bill from every provider has to include a procedure code for every service provided. These CPT (Current Procedural Terminology) codes are actually the property of the American Medical Association – and a significant source of revenue for the AMA through licensing arrangements. The AMA makes tens of millions of dollars annually selling the coding materials and conducting courses for hospitals, doctors, insurance companies and others. This is more than the AMA earns in member dues. So of course they want to preserve the use of these codes for as long as possible. ⇑

Compare this sorry state of affairs with your printed or online bank statements. Copies of checks are provided; every debit and credit is explained. Ditto with your credit card. *How can banking, which handles trillions of transactions a day, be so clear, while health care is so opaque?* Are health care companies incompetent? Of course not. The difference is that up until recently, the average consumer-patient didn't care because it wasn't your money. But increasingly, it is.

One patient profiled in the New York Times received a $132,000 hospital bill. According to the medical billing advocate who helped this patient, "There were three explanations of benefits from Blue Cross Blue Shield, each with an different amount due," ranging from about $164 to $81,900.[44] All told, the advocate spent about 96 hours dissecting these bills, line by line, comparing it with the providers' medical records and tracking it all in a spreadsheet. Ultimately, the patient owed exactly $164.99.

So is this a conspiracy? Are the health plans and providers out to get us? No, but it is a direct result of the basic, flawed incentives in the industry.

hospitals bill insurers to make up for losses of treating uninsured and federally insured patients (lower reimbursement rate)

Price-fixing specialists

While on the subject of the AMA's role in creating and managing the procedure codes negotiated between plans and providers, let's look at how the base prices of medical services are actually set. These prices are established in part on recommendations from the Relative Value Scale Update Committee (RUC), a group controlled by the AMA and staffed mostly by members of specialty societies. It's a top-down, highly bureaucratic approach, in which insiders are essentially able to "name their prices" simply because there are no market mechanisms to counter them. In other industries, it might simply be called price-fixing. In health care, it's business as usual.

Why? Because the RUC simply makes recommendations to Medicare, and it's up to the government to accept these recommendations or suggest alternatives. And for the past decades, successive governments have simply yielded to the recommendations. After all, if they suggested alternatives, these would be open to public comment, and who do you think would comment? The AMA and all the medical specialties, of course. And do you think they would comment positively on the alternatives?

This system of price setting has hugely negative effects, because some RUC time estimates for specific tasks have proven to be vastly overstated, leading to unaccountably high costs. For example, some research suggests it takes about five minutes to read an echocardiogram. The RUC estimates 30 minutes. Why does this matter? It allows providers to bill twelve claims an hour for this task, instead of two … but it's priced for two an hour!!

The RUC has also favored specialists at the expense of generalists, at great cost to society.[45] While specialists are robustly compensated for the procedures they perform, primary care physicians earn much less overall, and often earn nothing at all for "cognitive services" such as patient counseling. This, of course, is often the very thing patients need most. As a result, graduating medical students, typically saddled with massive loan debt, are flocking to the specialties that have the highest fee schedules.

Over the past 10 years, according to the American Academy of Family Physicians (AAFP), 90% of medical school graduates have chosen to enter higher-paid specialties like orthopedic surgery, radiology and dermatology. Only 10% have chosen primary care. This has fueled a large and growing shortage of primary care physicians; AAFP says we'll be short 39,000 nationwide by 2020.[46]

will be replaced w/ PAs & NPs

* * *

The Cure: Talk to your representatives and senators about banning the RUC and replacing it with a subcommittee of the Medicare Payment Advisory Committee (MedPAC). This is an independent agency established to advise Congress on issues affecting the Medicare program, including access to care, quality of care, and more. This group would likely bring more openness, common sense, fairness, and diversity of experience – and less self-interest – to the pricing equation. Only Congress can fix this problem, and only you can fix Congress.

* * *

A thoroughly dysfunctional market

The bottom line in all this: Pricing in the health care industry bears little relation to what we would commonly understand as a functioning market. In actual markets, buyers make rational purchasing decisions for goods and services based on a clear understanding of their cost and quality. And sellers compete vigorously on that basis as well. Typically, the seller who offers the highest quality product at the lowest price wins. And consumers who have that information win too.

Now consider the companies that manufacture supplies – knee implants, pacemakers, crutches, bandages, and so on – to clinicians and medical facilities. In a functioning market, these companies would have a strong incentive to be less expensive than their competitors. But the simple wisdom that governs all other markets often doesn't apply to health care. Why? If the hospital simply passes the cost through to the insurer, who then passes all or some of that cost on to the patient, there's little incentive for the hospital to negotiate discounts. And of course the sellers know this.

For example, the Government Accounting Office did a large study on the wide price variations for knee and hip implants (the device the surgeon puts in when replacing a knee or hip).[47] The GAO found nothing that could possibly explain these variations. Their conclusion: Manufacturers were simply charging whatever they could, to whomever they could, with no real market forces to provide the pricing discipline we see in other industries. *So instead of a competition to supply high quality goods at the lowest cost, it's more like a competition to supply them at the highest cost. And once more, it's patients who ultimately pay the price.*

This chaos is reflected in a book by Amanda Bennett, a Pulitzer Prize-winning journalist, called *The Cost of Hope*.[48] It's a poignant memoir of her relationship with her husband, Terence Foley, from their initial meeting in China through his death from a rare form of kidney cancer. It's also a detailed account of one family's long and often perplexing journey through the health care maze. In one vivid passage, Bennett describes payers and providers "bargaining like car salesmen or Chinese vendors – naming ridiculous prices that have no bearing on reality" while those actually paying the bills had no say in the process.

That's the problem in a nutshell. When purchasing decisions are made in the dark, and prices are based on nothing more than what the seller can get in any given situation, the inefficiencies are enormous. Bennett reports that, over the course of his care, Foley received 76 CAT scans, with prices ranging from $550 to $3,232. "Since none of us had to account for the cost of these procedures," she writes, "all of us, doctors and patients alike, could casually afford to pop them like cherry Twizzlers."

A simple example of how things should work

Just when you might feel ready to throw your arms up and surrender, an organization like Baptist Health System in San Antonio, Texas, comes along to point the way forward. Believe it or not, bringing rationality to an irrational health care industry really isn't all that difficult. Baptist recently joined with Medicare in a new initiative around hip and knee replacements. Instead of paying separately for hospital costs, surgical costs, professional services costs, and all the other costs, Baptist and Medicare negotiated a single price that included all costs for the procedure, including the implant.[49] BUNDLING

Once the deal was signed, Baptist had a heart-to-heart talk with the surgeons who perform these procedures. The surgeons were offered a deal: If you can work together to bring the total supply costs for each surgery down below what the hospital gets paid, you can all share the rewards. The surgeons agreed, and notified their implant suppliers that all buying decisions would now be made by the hospital.

First, Baptist decided to consolidate the purchasing to just a few suppliers whose implants were all of the same good quality. Next, the hospital met with each manufacturer to lay out its new purchasing plan.

Baptist set up an auction site where each manufacturer could bid a price for its implant. In these auctions, a monitor showed who was the least expensive bidder, and ranked everyone else below. The manufacturers had two hours to bid, and could bid as many times as they liked. However, they could not know the prices others were bidding; all they could see was their rank. Because they knew the most expensive bidders would be eliminated, the incentives to keep those bids low were clear. *The results were dramatic. The first year, implant costs were cut an average of one-third. The next year they were cut even further.*[50, 51]

For the most part, Medicare is precluded from using the same basic competitive bidding process as Baptist. But a recent "demonstration project" showed the powerful benefits of such an approach – in 2011, such competitive bidding reduced Medicare spending on medical equipment such as wheelchairs by more than 42%.[52] The Affordable Care Act requires Medicare to expand competitive bidding for equipment, prosthetics, orthotics, and supplies by 2016.

It's a good step forward, but a little too narrow in scope and a little too slow to begin. Medicare should implement this program nationwide immediately, and extend it to medical devices, laboratory tests, radiologic diagnostic services, and other equipment and services as soon as possible.

* * *

The Cure: Talk to your Congressional Representatives about the Medicare bidding program. Ask them to accelerate the rapid deployment of that program, starting now.

* * *

Patients have a role too ... but we need help

Once the incentives are adjusted, we see how insurers, hospitals, and physicians can come together to make the system work more efficiently. In the Baptist example, each party benefits – hospitals and insurers collaborate to simplify purchasing and cut costs, and physicians share in those savings.

Patients need to adjust their behavior as well.

To illustrate: Why are more C-sections being performed today for low-risk pregnancies? One, providers get paid more for them. Two, more patients are requesting them because they value the convenience, and often don't bear the full cost of that decision – a C-section typically requires more hospital time and costs more than a vaginal birth. So the incentives for both providers and patients lead to decisions that bring higher costs, and, in many cases, worse outcomes.[53, 54]

While patients may not like them, high deductible health plans are making a difference, because they inevitably push patients to demand less expensive care, and avoid unnecessary tests and procedures. But the real key is information. Clear, reliable cost information must be brought into the light, so patients can better understand how to make some trade-offs.

We believe health care providers and insurers have an obligation to make this available, and lay out the patient's actual out-of-pocket expenses in an easily understandable manner. Simply stated, *patients need easy access to the kind of cost and quality information that drives purchasing decisions in every other industry* (more on this in Chapter 5). You don't buy anything – a car, a hammer, a gallon of milk – without knowing the cost. Why should health care be different?

It's happening, slowly. Insurers such as Aetna and states like New Hampshire are leading the way in helping consumer-patients identify and plan for the costs of medical procedures. But this information, tailored to each plan member's specific benefit design and network options, must be available to all patients, everywhere. In fact, it should be the law of the land.

* * *

The Cure: Work with your state legislators to introduce a bill that would guarantee a consumer's right to pricing information. In particular, a health plan (including Medicare and Medicaid) should have an obligation to provide an enrolled health plan member with timely, accurate and complete information on the expected out-of-pocket cost liability related to a defined episode of medical care. Such episodes should include, at a minimum, (1) elective procedures such as cardiac stents, screening colonoscopies, joint replacements; (2) chronic conditions such as diabetes, asthma, chronic heart failure; (3) acute events such as cancer. Information about the expected out-of-pocket cost should consider the plan member's benefit coverage rules, account for stipulated limits and past expenses applied to those limits. The health plan should also provide the plan member with such information by provider, facility or health system within the plan member's network to help the plan member select the highest value provider.

* * *

A Consumer-Patient's Right To Pricing Information

A 2011 Government Accounting Office report on Health Care Price Transparency concluded that "meaningful price information is difficult for consumers to obtain prior to receiving care."[55] Why is this important? Because according to the 2012 Kaiser Family Foundation survey of employer health care coverage, one in four employees in small firms, and one in five employees for all firms, were covered by a high deductible/high co-insurance plan.[10] As a result, a growing portion of consumer-patients need to fully understand and plan for the health care expenses they will incur when undergoing medical procedures. They need upfront information, tailored to each plan member, and incorporating their specific benefit design and network options.

For example, using the NH Health Cost site for New Hampshire residents, recent estimated out-of-pocket expenses related to a normal vaginal birth and new baby care for a plan member covered by Anthem, with a $1,000 deductible and 20% co-insurance, varied from $2,400 to $3,900 depending on the facility. Without this information, this consumer could pay much more than she needs to – and never even know it.

Many states have pushed for and adopted legislation that institutes central claims data repositories, to which public and private sector payers contribute. And these data are often used to publish comparative information on the costs and quality of certain standard procedures, inpatient and outpatient, by facility or provider organization.

However, these state efforts fall short of providing an individual consumer-patient with the specific expected cost for a medical episode of care, at the point of need, in a comparative form. That's because only the health plan sponsor can provide this information. The plan sponsor tracks the deductible already applied to past services, as well as the limits to out-of-pocket expenses. The plan sponsor also knows the current negotiated fees contracted with each provider in the network. Statewide efforts, by contrast, contain historical data and can only provide broad estimates to an individual consumer. (The New Hampshire site is a rare exception.) In the example above, the potential swing in out-of-pocket expenses for the patient is $1,500 – several weeks' worth of take-home net pay for an average employee. With so many employees now enrolled in high deductible/high co-insurance plans, having precise information on the expected financial liability associated to an episode of care is a necessity, not a luxury.

Chapter 4 – Creative Disruption

Can innovation save us?

Medical miracles occur every day, driven by innovations we could scarcely have imagined a generation ago. Think of the handheld sonograms that can image a heart and show the clinician if there's a blockage or leak in blood flow. Until recently, that information could only have been obtained through a long, invasive and potentially complicated procedure. Or consider the sensors that can monitor a diabetic's blood sugar and auto-regulate the amount of insulin in the body. There are many other examples, and they're amazing. *When great clinicians are supported by great technologies, truly great care is often the result.* And the future looks even more remarkable.

Progress in fields like genomics, proteomics (the study of protein structures and functions) and other "omics" promise to take the state of care to an entirely different level. Some believe we are on the verge of a new wave of medicine, in which even many of today's most advanced treatments will seem primitive in comparison. In his book *The Creative Destruction of Medicine: How the Digital Revolution Will Create Better Health Care,* Dr. Eric Topol lays out an exciting vision.[56] Topol argues that the convergence of two fields – genomics, with its ability to sequence a person's entire genetic code, and wireless, with its innovative health care apps – will be the key to transforming medicine. In Topol's view, health care has been too slow to embrace the digital communication technologies that have transformed other industries. He believes medicine's next frontier is a digital infrastructure that embraces genomics, wireless biosensors, advanced imaging and other innovations to make medicine more personalized and precise.

Much of today's care "doesn't recognize the individuality of people," says Topol. "By applying biosensors to the body, we can measure any physiologic metric – blood pressure, glucose, oxygen concentration in the blood – and send the data wirelessly through smart phones to doctors. That means you have this panoramic, high-definition, relatively comprehensive view of a patient that doctors can use to assess and manage disease, and that patients can use to help maintain their health and direct their own care."

It's a very big idea, with seemingly unlimited potential to improve treatments, extend lives and manage disease more effectively.

But will it help control costs? Hard to say. In this industry, it doesn't always work that way.

In health care, innovation doesn't necessarily reduce costs

Clayton Christensen, one of the great business thinkers of our time, has devoted much of his professional life to studying innovation.[57] Working with two physician colleagues, Christensen examined the health care industry through that prism, and came to a conclusion that seems surprising, if not downright counterintuitive: In health care, innovation and competition most often drive prices up, rather than down.

How can this be? Everyone knows these are the very forces that reduce costs and benefit consumers in other industries. Each year, for example, computers and other electronic devices get more powerful and less expensive. But these products exist in rational markets, where buyers and sellers come together based on transparent cost and quality information. As we've seen, that description does not apply to health care.

According to Christensen, innovation and competition actually increase health care prices because "bringing better, higher-priced products to market is more profitable. Hospital vs. hospital competition causes providers to expand their scope and offer more premium-priced services. Equipment suppliers boost the capability and cost of their machines and devices. Drug makers develop products that bring the highest prices. It's because we have such competition, not because we lack it, that health costs are rising."[58]

Is Christensen saying we should just stop innovating and competing? Of course not. Drawing on his knowledge of other industries, he says we need a new focus of innovation, one that transforms the actual delivery of care. Specifically, he says *we need to change our ideas of where care should be delivered, how it should be delivered, and who should deliver it.*

Unfortunately, as we've explained in the prior chapter … it's the incentives, stupid! As long as we continue to pay for every service delivered instead of the outcomes of those services, we'll remain stuck with higher costs and mediocre quality. Paying for the value of care received is the only way to ensure that the true disruptive forces of innovation play out in health care the same way as they do in other industries.

* * *

The Cure: Employers and individuals should only enroll in health plans that have converted a majority of payments to being value-based. Catalyst For Payment Reform is creating a health plan scorecard to that effect. Look for it, and use it in making decisions on which plans to enroll in. Reward the plans that are moving aggressively away from fee-for-service and punish the ones that aren't.

* * *

We must let innovation flourish at all levels of health care, not just technology

Christensen knows, in part from his own serious illness, that complex medical issues require our most advanced technologies and best medical minds. When a patient's life (or quality of life) hangs in the balance, cost is the last thing we should think about. But many conditions are very well understood, even routine, and can be managed without deep clinical expertise or costly equipment. As a result, Christensen thinks expensive hospital care should be restricted to only the most serious cases. In industry after industry, he's observed how smaller, lower-cost suppliers take business away from bigger, more expensive competitors. He thinks inexpensive clinics can – and should – do the same to hospitals, if given a fair chance.

"The type of competition that brings prices down is disruptive innovation," says Christensen. "Disruption in health care entails moving the simplest procedures now performed in expensive hospitals to outpatient clinics, retail clinics, and patients' homes. Costs will drop as more of the tasks performed only by doctors shift to nurses and physicians' assistants. Hoping that our hospitals and doctors will become cheap won't make health care more affordable and accessible, but a move toward lower-cost venues and lower-cost caregivers will."[58] For hospitals, which earn almost half their revenues from outpatient care, Christensen's ideas are problematic. But within the industry, the prospect of hospitals getting smaller, and more care shifting to less costly settings, is considered inevitable. And why not empower nurses to do more?

"You don't need a medical degree to provide primary care, and you haven't for more than 100 years," says Susan Apold, health policy director at the American College of Nurse Practitioners. This may seem an overstatement (especially to primary care docs!), but nurses can certainly perform many care functions at a lower cost. Certified Nurse Practitioners can already prescribe medication in 16 states and Washington, DC. But elsewhere, restrictive state "scope-of-practice" laws prevent non-physician clinicians from practicing to the full extent of their training; *34 states do not allow even the best-trained nurses to practice without physician supervision.*[59]

Giving nurses more power to supplement the efforts of physicians, who are already stretched too thin, is a common-sense step in the right direction. This would expand the workforce supply, and provide the kind of increased competition that actually could bring costs down.

* * *

The Cure: Talk to your state legislators and encourage them to sponsor legislation that will ensure all clinicians can practice to the full extent of their professional credentialing and meet the scope of-practice standards recommended by the Institute of Medicine. The IOM says "nurses should practice to the full extent of their education and training" and be "full partners, with physicians and other health care professionals, in redesigning health care in the United States."[59] We agree.

* * *

The first battlefront: Medicare

Clay Christensen's ideas represent the kind of thinking we need to apply on a massive scale, in line with the massive threat posed by uncontrolled health care spending. Solving this problem is a national project that will require the efforts of all citizens. We are all participants in the system, and each of us owns a stake in its success or failure. This is not about politics. It's about doing the right things to protect your family and your wealth, and in the process helping the country out of its fiscal mess. And that will never happen unless we rapidly reform incentives in Medicare.

By flipping the incentives that cause the rampant waste and inefficiency described in earlier chapters, we believe Medicare expenses per patient could actually be frozen for the next decade. As we saw earlier, Medicare spending per patient in some areas of the country is roughly half that of other regions, not because beneficiaries living there are getting worst quality care. In fact, the opposite is true. A landmark research by the folks at Dartmouth showed that quality of care actually decreases in the areas of the country with greater than average per capita spending. "Nearly thirty per cent of Medicare's costs could be saved without negatively affecting health outcomes if spending in high- and medium-cost areas could be reduced to the level in low-cost areas," says Peter Orszag, President Obama's former budget director.[31]

Let's be clear. As more Americans qualify for Medicare, we obviously expect total care costs to go up. But we believe the amount spent per Medicare beneficiary can stay about the same as it is today, and give American households an opportunity to recoup some of the income lost to runaway health care cost inflation.

The Medicare program, controlled by the federal government, is the country's largest purchaser of health care services. Yet, in critical ways, Medicare is prohibited from using its purchasing power. For example, Medicare cannot, by law, negotiate directly with drug companies over medication prices for Medicare beneficiaries. Yes, you read that right. The buyer cannot negotiate with the seller. By law. And as we mentioned in a prior chapter, Medicare has only a limited ability to use competitive bidding to purchase health care services and supplies. This has to change.

However, this will be a bare-knuckle battle against the forces of the status quo (like pharmaceutical companies and all those whose wallets keep getting fatter while ours get thinner), and we must not give up until the change is completed.

* * *

The Cure: Push Congress to enact legislation authorizing Medicare to change the way it pays for and covers services, based on the recommendations of the Medicare Payment Advisory Commission (MedPAC) and the results of Medicare's ongoing payment experiments. In addition, as MedPAC notes, the Medicare fee-for-service benefit package has remained essentially unchanged since the program was created in 1965, and should be substantially changed to control costs for beneficiaries and taxpayers alike.[60]

* * *

Bundled payments can help everyone win

Under fee-for-service, every market signal screams out to doctors: Do not collaborate on that patient's care. Order that extra test. Recommend one more procedure. Fill that hospital bed. After all, doctors are human and respond to economic signals like everyone else. But bundled payment programs offer a different model. Compensation is tied to the value of care delivered, not the volume of services. Providers are given a fixed overall budget for a patient's specific episode of medical care. If they manage that care well and come in under budget, everyone wins.

It's a fundamental re-thinking of the relationship between health insurance and health care. For example, PROMETHEUS Payment is a bundled payment program now being piloted around the country. Its purpose is to reward excellent care and control costs for chronic conditions, hospitalizations and other procedures – and remove incentives that reward providers financially when patients get unnecessary care or are re-admitted to the hospital. Instead, the incentives encourage doctors to collaborate with each other and provide good outcomes, and the better the care, the more they can earn.[61]

In other words, **bundled payment aligns economic incentives with clinicians' strong desire to improve patient health.** In doing so, it creates an environment where doing the right things for patients helps providers and insurers do well financially. It also helps make price and quality information transparent and easily available. As a result, these kinds of programs can help transform today's fragmented and inefficient system into one that is far more integrated and accountable.

Just as important, if not more so, bundled payments are total negotiated prices for a medical episode of care. What does that mean? It means that whether you need a knee replacement, are having a baby, or simply need your chronic care managed for this coming year, you should be able to see, up front, what the total price for that care will be. As a result, your health plan should be able to tell you very specifically how much your total share of that cost will be. No exceptions, no surprises. That's what we're fighting for.

* * *

The Cure: In the new health insurance exchanges mandated by the Affordable Care Act, each state and Congress should require health plans to specify their level of involvement in new payment programs. In addition, as a consumer, you should demand to have the full and complete price of every elective and non-emergent medical episode cost of care, including comparative pricing by provider, and specific estimates of total out-of-pocket expenses. This right should apply to all health plans, including those in the exchanges and Medicare.

* * *

Bundled payments give birth to an orthopedic surgery center of excellence.

There's nothing extraordinary about Dr. Scott Schoifet (pronounced show-fet), but he achieves extraordinary results. Like many orthopedic surgeons, he performs about 200 surgeries a year – mostly hips and knees. Two years ago Dr. Schoifet and a few other orthopedic surgeons in New Jersey started a pilot project with Horizon Blue Cross Blue Shield. The goal was to create a single budget, adjusted to the severity of each patient, that would cover an entire episode of medical care, from the decision to have the surgery, to ninety days after the surgery. And if (1) the quality of care met all the agreed-upon metrics, and (2) the costs came in under budget, the surgeon would get the difference between the budget and the actual costs. The potential sources of savings were pretty clear: first, the costs of the implants, which vary significantly between hospitals, and second the costs after surgery, which can include readmissions when there's a problem.

It didn't take long for Dr. Schoifet to realize that he could take on the full responsibility for the patient and deliver better care at a lower cost than when there were a bunch of uncoordinated hand-offs – physician to hospital, hospital to rehab, rehab to physician. So he and a few of his colleagues set out to create a "center of excellence", or a "focused factory" as Harvard Business School professor Regina Herzlinger calls it.

In his center of excellence, Dr. Schiofet (like Dr. Monk Elmer, whom we'll profile in a moment), can make sure that standard processes and procedures are all in place to make sure that errors aren't committed, patients receive all the attention they need, and care is well coordinated. It's a simple formula, but until he started getting paid under bundled payment arrangements, Dr. Schiofet was simply playing the game as it was designed. Now it's a new game, and this one is for the benefit of the patient, in addition to rewarding the physician when value is delivered.

The second battlefront: politics at the mercy of money

How is it possible that Medicare cannot negotiate the costs of prescription drugs? Why are government agencies forbidden from conducting cost-effectiveness studies before approving a new device or pill? Why can't Medicare competitively bid orthopedic or cardiac implantable devices? Follow the money trail. In recent years, the pharmaceutical and health products industry has spent billions of dollars on lobbying and campaign contributions. You can be sure very little of it was spent with your needs in mind. But that kind of cash can sure buy a lot of favorable votes and regulations.

For politicians, money talks louder than ever. In 2010, the average cost of winning an election to the House of Representatives was $1.4 million and the average cost of winning a Senate election was nearly $9 million.[62] Most of this money comes from wealthy entrenched groups with agendas to protect. They bankroll the candidates most likely to further those interests, push hard for legislation they like, and often get what they pay for.

Every year the lobbying groups that represent hospitals, insurers, physicians, pharmaceutical companies, medical device manufacturers and others shower Washington, DC, with billions to get a bill passed or defeated. For example, hundreds of millions of dollars were spent either supporting or trying to defeat the Affordable Care Act.[63]

The point is not that some groups opposed a critical bill and other groups supported it. After all, that's just democracy. *The point is that very well funded, very powerful groups are fighting vigorously every day to protect their interests. Occasionally those interests may coincide with those of the average patient. Most often, they don't.*

And it's a lot easier for these lobbyists to influence policymakers with the current mess of flawed incentives. However, if Medicare were able to establish bidding auctions for prescription drugs, medical devices, and other supplies it currently pays for fee-for-service, and if those bids were conducted by an independent third party, like the Government Accounting Office, or the Office of the Actuary, the actions of lobbyists would matter far less.

That's why we need to unleash the true purchasing power of Medicare and that of the millions of Americans covered by public or private health insurance. And that's what the agents of the status quo want to block. But no one in the history of this country has ever been able to block the collective will of the American people. It really is up to us to make the change we want to see happen.

To fight back, embrace those willing to take some financial responsibility for managing your care, instead of just hitting you for an extra buck

While interest groups spend billions to bend the health care system to their needs, you, in your own way, can do the same. And collectively we can bend the system back into our favor.

First, as discussed, you can seek out the provider organizations in your area that are known innovators. Many around the country – Geisinger in Pennsylvania, ThedaCare in Wisconsin, Virginia Mason in Washington, Atrius in Massachusetts – are widely recognized for providing systematic, high quality care. These are forerunners of what's come to be known as the Accountable Care Organization, or ACO. It's become a bit of a buzzword that can mean different things to different people. But generally, an ACO is an organization in which doctors, hospitals and other providers come together to coordinate care and improve efficiencies, in exchange for the chance to earn common financial incentives.[64, 65]

These providers focus on communicating with each other, partnering with patients in making treatment decisions, and consuming medical resources wisely based on best care practices. As a result, they often provide better patient care at lower costs. And when they do, the providers do well too, since many ACOs tie provider reimbursements to quality measures and reductions in total care costs. In recent years, more employers have become aware of these advantages, and begun offering ACO-style options to their employees. However, there are true ACOs and there are wannabes. The real innovators are the ones willing to take direct financial responsibility for your care.

There are others who prefer not to put a label on it, but do the work just as well. You can usually tell by asking some simple questions. Do you get paid more if you do more tests on me, or if I have better outcomes? Do you constantly monitor your patient's results? Do you have a quality dashboard (a toolset to provide relevant, timely information and help enhance patient care)? Do you know your readmission rate? If you like the answers, reward them with your business. If not, walk away, because they're just pretenders. After all, if they don't know how well they're managing patients and can't provide you with real numbers, how good can they really be?

* * *

The Cure: Markets work when consumers vote with their feet. The high performing health systems and physician practices in your area should be rewarded with more business – your business, your health plan's business. Punish the pretenders and reward the real innovators.

* * *

Monk Elmer, a country doc from Wisconsin, is the real deal.

As he describes it, Dr. Elmer's practice is certainly not an ordinary one. Patients are seen, on average, for 20 minutes. There's hardly ever a wait time. Lab tests are done before the patient is seen by the physician, and the results are available within 10 minutes, while the patient is still being seen. If a simple routine procedure such as the removal of a mole is needed, Dr. Elmer pushes a button, a nurse or physician assistant comes in, takes the doctor's request and comes back within a minute with the necessary kit. Patient satisfaction is at an all-time high and the practice enjoys the highest quality scores in all of Wisconsin.

How is such a transformation possible? Simply by following the same type of process reengineering techniques that have been applied to almost every other industry to reduce waste and inefficiency, known as LEAN/Six Sigma. The results are astonishing. Dr. Elmer spends more time with each patient than he used to, sees fewer each day than he used to, but the practice's net income is up. Why? Because they don't waste any more resources. They don't spend time chasing a simple surgery kit, or chasing after patient to get lab tests done, or worrying about scheduling. Instead, they've optimized all these simple processes so that they work as efficiently as possible...to the benefit of the patient. Think about it. When's the last time you had the results of a lab test that was taken in the doctor's office before you left that office, so you could have a discussion about the results with the doctor? In my case the answer is never.

Yes, health care is different, but redesigning the simple tasks that are so inefficient today is just one way to improve outcomes for everyone. So why doesn't every practice in the country function like Dr. Elmer's? You got it...it's the incentives.

Progress to be sure, but miles still to go

In many industries, creative destruction has had a transformative effect, enhancing quality and efficiency, and benefitting consumers in the process. Can it happen in health care? Obviously, this is an industry unlike any other. Medicine is a distinctively complex art and science. Solutions are often elusive and imperfect, and issues of life and death can never be reduced to simple business metrics. As a result, the health care market will never be as precisely efficient as others.

But it can be so much better. Every day, millions of patients are helped in small and big ways by skilled hands supported by incredible technologies. And, unfortunately, every day, just as many may fall through the cracks. They never get a call from their doctor or nurse. They never get a reminder about an important screening. They never get coaching that can help improve their lifestyle habits. They suffer from the incentives that encourage many to do the wrong thing for the patient.

Ultimately, the same data-driven techniques and metrics that have transformed other industries may do the same for health care. In this regard, we have actually come a long way in the last ten years or so. While we still have very far to go, a better future is starting to come into view.

Chapter 5 – Unleash the Consumer-patient

You can't make a market without data

In every other sector of the economy, companies either deliver value or go out of business. To demonstrate that value, they compete directly with each other and offer transparent information about the price and quality of their goods and services. *But in health care, patients are constantly required to make major purchasing decisions with little or no knowledge of price or quality.*

It's hard to overstate how big a problem this is. In health care, prices often bear no relation to any kind of market reality because they are cloaked in secrecy. Recent studies in California and Massachusetts found that common procedures done mainly in hospitals, such as a hysterectomy or gallbladder removal could vary tenfold, depending on your insurer.[66] Of course, the highest price was charged to the lowest person on the totem pole – the self-pay uninsured. Even routine procedures like a colonoscopy can range from $350 to $5,805 depending on where it's performed, whether a patient is fully sedated or has localized anesthesia, and whether more than one procedure is done in the same sitting.

In no other market are customers blindly charged such vastly different prices for identical goods and services. Nobody walks into a new car lot and pays ten times more than the next guy for the same vehicle, simply because no one told him what that cost would be. Because in other "retail" markets, prices are transparent and can be thoroughly researched and compared online.

So why are prices mostly hidden from consumer-patients? After all, is it that difficult for health plans or providers to calculate these prices?

It actually isn't very complicated to calculate these prices, and some health insurers like Aetna have developed good tools to provide plan members with accurate estimates of out-of-pocket expenses for certain health care services, showing variations in that price by physicians and hospitals in the network. As mentioned, the state of New Hampshire has also taken a leading role by setting up a public website that provides estimates on certain common procedures. NH Health Cost compares actual prices for individual members of specific health plans, from providers in that plan's network. It's a great resource for residents of the Granite State, but according to a Government Accounting Office report from 2011, Aetna and New Hampshire had the only two sites in the land that were somewhat comprehensive in providing pricing information to consumer-patients.[55]

So why aren't others doing it? For one, some health plans consider the discounts they've negotiated to be "trade secrets" and don't want other health plans to know about them. And then, some provider organizations, mostly hospitals, insert clauses in their contracts with health plans that specifically forbid those plans to disclose the pricing they've negotiated, or to use that price as a mechanism to activate plan members. Think about it. Health plans and providers are purposefully hiding pricing information from you. It's not that they can't disclose price data. They just won't.

So the health care marketplace can't function as a normal market because consumers are purposefully locked out from making value-based decisions. The good news is that large employers have started rebelling against these practices (see CastLight story), but ultimately it's up to every American to demand the right to complete and accurate information on the price and quality of the care they will get. Organizations like Costs of Care and Healthcare Blue Book are also fighting to provide consumer-patients with the information that they need, and you should support them.

Beyond privately insured Americans, pricing transparency must also come to Medicare. While the feds might argue that the price for each service in Medicare is fixed (which is true), the total number of services used in a common procedure like a colonoscopy or a hysterectomy varies widely, and that impacts the total price of the procedure to the Medicare beneficiary. As such, tools like Healthcare Blue Book or CastLight should be made available to all Medicare beneficiaries now. This will help the 40-million-plus Americans in that program become the great force of change they can be, if only armed with the right information.

It ain't that hard to light up the darkened health care market

Founded only a few years ago, CastLight Health is focused on a simple mission: providing health plan members with actionable information on their cost of accessing certain health care services.

In response to the rising and inexorable tide of high deductible, high co-insurance health insurance plans, employers realized that they had to arm employees and their family members with more specific information on their out-of-pocket expenses, especially when the decision involved big ticket items like a joint replacement or having a baby. And since this information wasn't forthcoming from the health plans, the employers started looking for a solution elsewhere, and that's where CastLight came in.

Using information from past medical bills paid by the employer's health plans, CastLight was able to form a picture of the average cost for some procedures, and many services, across the network of physicians and hospitals used by employees and their families. Basically, CastLight reproduced what NH Health Cost was doing, but went one step further. Since the employer is able to feed CastLight the specific benefit design for each employee, and, further, since CastLight can get up-to-date information on how much of the deductible the employee might have used, the estimates of out-of-pocket costs for any individual become far more precise and specific. As a result, consumer-patients have been empowered to make far better decisions – this comparative information can save an employee hundreds of dollars by seeking care from a lower priced hospital or physician.

Patients must be agents of change, and common sense incentives can help

It's long been understood that patients will only become active consumers of health care when their decisions begin to impact their wallets and care options directly. In this age of benefit buy-downs and high-deductible health plans, that time has arrived. *Patients now have little choice but to get informed and start applying the same kind of decision-making to health care as they do to other major purchases.* Not in every situation, of course – no one in an acute crisis is going to, or should, stop and research emergency room costs. But when patients are able to compare providers and treatment options directly across a wide range of situations, the prospect of real and lasting change becomes clear.

Indeed, in health care, we are beginning to see the type of knowledge shift that happened long ago in other industries. For instance, the idea of a computer in every household was once considered pure fantasy. Only experts needed computers, the thinking went, or had the ability to use them. But after a long series of disruptive innovations, computers are ubiquitous, fit in the palm of a hand, and it's hard to imagine how we lived so long without them. A similar transformation is slowly taking hold in health care, with knowledge no longer restricted to the few, but dispersed widely among the many.

Patients will also need to get smarter about the everyday decisions that affect their care. Making healthy exercise and diet choices, managing chronic conditions wisely, getting recommended screenings, using generic drugs whenever possible, avoiding emergency rooms for non-emergencies, maintaining a relationship with a primary care doctor ... these are the kinds of simple, common sense actions that can keep us healthier and save billions of dollars in unnecessary health care expenses.

we're irrational, but especially in the complexities of health decisions - a delayed gratificati[on]

Of course, many patients will never do the logical things they should to get well and stay well. It's just human nature. We all know smoking kills, yet millions still smoke. We all know driving without a seat belt greatly increases risks, yet many still go without. The World Health Organization calls tanning beds "carcinogenic to humans," yet this remains a multi-billion dollar industry. *People who make bad choices cost the system dearly, and often suffer avoidable complications that make bad situations worse. But there are ways to encourage healthier behaviors.*

Think of how auto insurance works. When police and insurers began sharing traffic ticket information with the Department of Motor Vehicles, getting a ticket became far more costly. Today, points taken off a license can lead to the suspension of driving privileges and significantly higher insurance premiums. As a result, drivers have every incentive to be careful and prudent on the road.

because health is a moral good

Health insurance plans, on the other hand, haven't gotten this right yet, at least not for the vast majority of Americans who get their coverage from employers. Other than penalties for smokers, employer-based health insurance generally doesn't distinguish the *✗ "good drivers" from the "bad drivers." A plan member either has a large upfront deductible, or some co-insurance every time he gets care, or both. But these cost-sharing mechanisms fail to distinguish between the types of plan members who might access care more often and those who may be more occasional users. One flaw in the Affordable Care Act is that, by prohibiting insurers from considering health risks when setting rates, it gives people no incentive to lower their premiums by getting healthier. *controlling risk pools*

Yes, it's a slippery slope. Where do we draw the line? Would obese people pay more for their health insurance? What about those who have high blood pressure? Or don't get enough sleep? Or have family histories of certain diseases? For many, the ethics of treating health insurance this way are troubling. On the individual market, insurance companies have long discriminated against the less healthy by charging more or denying coverage altogether. The Affordable Care Act finally starts to put an end to that. Once most Americans are in the system, perhaps we can begin to have an adult discussion about linking health insurance costs to avoidable negative behaviors, and decide what we as a society are willing to call fair or unfair.

Will patients rise to the challenge?

Like any abused population, patients may understandably be wary of grand talk of change. They're used to being led by the nose through a system they neither understand nor respect. They've been over-charged, over-treated, under-informed and generally baffled by their health care for decades. They can't possibly be expected to develop the skills they need to be smart consumers of these services overnight. And in truth, during stressful times of illness or injury, how careful a shopper can anyone really be?

We've known for years that a small slice of the population drives most U.S. health care spending – about 10% of the population accounts for about 60% of total costs.[4] These very ill patients cannot and should not be expected to make cost a priority. But the rest of us, the lucky and relatively healthy 90%, can make a big difference. *We can make smart choices, and consider it our individual responsibility to recognize and question wasteful spending whenever we see it.* We can vote. We can agitate our leaders to grow a backbone and double down on the cost-saving provisions of the Affordable Care Act. We can educate ourselves, and push for more transparent information that lets us compare hospitals, reward the best performers, and use the power of the market to improve quality.

And we can embrace the new, by taking advantage of the many online and mobile tools that are becoming available to help us get and stay healthier. Recently there's been an explosion of e-health apps to help patients lose weight, stick to their meds, control blood sugar, quit smoking, improve their sleep and more, sometimes in highly innovative ways. For example, the GymPact app asks users to commit to visiting a gym a given number of times each week – and pay a small fee each time they skip. The app tracks users' gym attendance by GPS, and charges their credit cards if they don't go. These fees are then distributed to the members who keep their commitments. A little creepy? Perhaps. A strong positive incentive? Definitely. To be sure, not every patient will go for these types of tools. But their potential to encourage long-term lifestyle changes at a very low cost is an exciting, perhaps even transformative development. And it's just getting started.

The Incentive Cure

In these pages, we have tried to provide a concise summary of how, and why, the U.S. health care industry fails so many of its citizens. We have also tried to highlight some of the most promising ideas for change.

We have focused on incentives in the delivery system, because we believe that's the best way to understand why those within the industry behave the way they do.

- When a doctor orders more tests and procedures than you may need, she's acting rationally in her own interests – she earns more money and gains some protection against potential lawsuits.

- When a hospital refuses to disclose patient safety failures, it's acting rationally in its own interests – it would obviously prefer to keep that information from public view.

- When drug companies persuade lawmakers not to let Medicare negotiate prices, they're acting rationally in their own interests – they get to charge more for their products.

And on and on it goes. But of course the question is: *Who's looking out for your interests? For better or worse, that has to be your job.* We hope we've given you a solid understanding of the forces that make health care in the U.S. so inefficient and infuriating, and some ways to fight back for yourself, your family, and your country.

So, one more time: How does the world's greatest economic power spend twice as much on health care as any other industrialized nation, and get worse results? Let's review the long line of harmful incentives that have brought us to this state.

- Employers are encouraged by post-war tax breaks to provide workers with generous health insurance policies.
- Employees are encouraged by these policies to become passive consumers of health care services, because they only pay a small fraction of the costs.
- Providers of medical services are encouraged to keep cost and quality information hidden from those consumers, and make the market as opaque as possible.
- Those without insurance are encouraged to remain that way, because they know they can get "free" hospital care courtesy of the American taxpayer.
- Doctors and hospitals are encouraged by fee-for-service payment to deliver as many tests and treatments as possible, leading to rampant overutilization.
- They are also encouraged not to collaborate with each other, so each provider can bill as many services as possible.
- Hospitals are encouraged to take a less than rigorous approach to avoiding re-admissions, since every admission is an opportunity for more revenue.
- Farmers are encouraged by national agricultural policy to grow crops used to make low-priced junk food.

- Poor families are encouraged by those low prices to eat foods that cause obesity, diabetes and other chronic conditions that account for 75% of health care costs.
- Hospitals are encouraged to keep patient safety failures rates secret, because there are no repercussions to doing so or any government agency to investigate them.
- Medical students are encouraged by lopsided fee structures to become specialists instead of primary care doctors, leading to serious and growing shortages of the least expensive, most necessary care.
- Drug and medical device makers are encouraged to charge inflated prices to Medicare, because the Medicare program cannot by law negotiate those prices directly.
- Hospitals are encouraged not to manage supplier costs aggressively, because they simply pass those costs on to insurers, who then pass them on to consumers.
- Consumers are encouraged not to shop around for medical services, because the lack of transparent cost and quality information makes it virtually impossible – and someone else is usually footing the bill.
- Politicians are encouraged by the money and lobbying power of entrenched interests to resist sensible reforms.

And, amazingly, those who do well within the current system are encouraged to keep things pretty much the way they are. We all, individually and collectively, pay the price in blood and treasure for this travesty.

You need to get mad the same way we're mad and say no, hell no to the status quo. Nothing can stop a determined citizenry from making the change we all need, and that starts with you.

This is the fight of our generation because if we lose, the cost to future generations will be immense. But if we win, we transform the country for the better and truly propel it forward for the generations to come.

We're committed to this fight because we know how simple the incentive cure truly is:

1. Pay for value instead of volume to encourage physicians to do right.
2. Change health insurance benefit designs to encourage patients to do right.
3. Make all price and quality information easy to get and act upon, to create a real health care market.
4. Remove the regulatory and legislative barriers that impede payers and providers from innovating.

We've given you concrete action items to help implement this cure. Now, you're the physician and the health care system is the patient. Administer the cure, and don't let the patient off the hook.

References

1. Institute of Medicine [IOM]. Best care at lower cost: The path to continuously learning health care in America. Washington DC, 2012 Sept 6. Available at: http://www.iom.edu/Reports/2012/Best-Care-at-Lower-Cost-The-Path-to-Continuously-Learning-Health-Care-in-America.aspx

2. Herzberg F. One more time: How do you motivate employees? Harvard Business Review. 1987 Sept.-Oct.:87-99

3. Altarum Institute. Insights from monthly national health expenditure estimates through August 2012. Center for sustainable health spending: Health sector economic indicators, 2012 Oct. Available at: http://www.altarum.org/files/imce/CSHS-Spending-Brief_Oct 2012.pdf

4. Kaiser Family Foundation. Health care costs: A primer: Key information on health care costs and their impact. Washington DC, 2012 May. Available at: http://www.kff.org/insurance/7670.cfm

5. Murray CJ, Frenk J. Ranking 37th--measuring the performance of the United States health care system. N Engl J Med. 2010;362(2):98-9.

6. Davis K, Schoen C, Stremikis K. Mirror, mirror on the wall: How the performance of the United States health care system compares internationally, 2010 update. New York: The Commonwealth Fund, 2010 Jun. 23. Available at: http://www.commonwealthfund.org/Publications/Fund-Reports/2010/Jun/Mirror-Mirror-Update.aspx?page=all

7. Squires D. Explaining high health care spending in the United States: An international comparison of supply, utilization, prices, and quality. New York: The Commonwealth Fund, 2012 May 3.

Available at: http://www.commonwealthfund.org/Publications/Issue-Briefs/2012/May/High-Health-Care-Spending.aspx

8. Gray BH, Bowden T, Johansen I, et al. Electronic health records: An international perspective on "meaningful use". New York, NY: The Commonwealth Fund, 2011 Nov. 17. Available at: http://www.commonwealthfund.org/Publications/Issue-Briefs/2011/Nov/Electronic-Health-Records-International-Use.aspx

9. Spiro T, Lee EO, Emanuel EJ. Price and utilization: Why we must target both to curb health care costs. Ann Intern Med. 2012;157(8):586-90.

10. Kaiser Family Foundation, Health Research and Educational Trust. Employer health benefits: 2012 annual survey. Washington DC, 2012. Available at: http://ehbs.kff.org/

11. Flegal KM, Carroll MD, Kit BK, et al. Prevalence of obesity and trends in the distribution of body mass index among us adults, 1999-2010. JAMA. 2012;307(5):491-7.

12. Ogden CL, Carroll MD, Kit BK, et al. Prevalence of obesity and trends in body mass index among us children and adolescents, 1999-2010. JAMA. 2012;307(5):483-90.

13. Finkelstein EA, Trogdon JG, Cohen JW, et al. Annual medical spending attributable to obesity: Payer-and service-specific estimates. Health Aff (Millwood). 2009;28(5):w822-31.

14. Haviland AM, Marquis MS, McDevitt RD, et al. Growth of consumer-directed health plans to one-half of all employer-sponsored insurance could save $57 billion annually. Health Aff (Millwood). 2012;31(5):1009-15.

15. Starr P. The triumph of accommodation. The social transformation of american medicine: The rise of a sovereign profession and the making of a vast industry. New York: Basic Books; 1984.

16. Bjerga A. The making of the 1,000-page farm bill. Bloomberg Businessweek. 2012 June 28.Available at:

http://www.businessweek.com/articles/2012-06-28/the-making-of-the-1-000-page-farm-bill

17. Reddy KS, Patel V, Jha P, et al. Towards achievement of universal health care in India by 2020: A call to action. Lancet. 2011;377(9767):760-8.

18. Shetty P. Medical tourism booms in India, but at what cost? Lancet. 2010;376(9742):671-2.

19. Kavilanz P. Surgery and sightseeing on your boss' dime. CNN Money. 2010 Aug. 11.Available at: http://money.cnn.com/2010/08/11/news/companies/health_care_medical_travel/index.htm

20. Kohn LT, Corrigan J, Donaldson MS, et al. To err is human: Building a safer health system. Washington DC: National Academy Press; 1999.

21. Institute of Medicine [IOM]. Crossing the quality chasm: A new health system for the 21st century. National Academy of Sciences Press, 2001. Available at: http://books.nap.edu/catalog/10027.html

22. Health Research and Educational Trust. Reducing avoidable hospital readmissions. Agency for Health Care Research and Quality [AHRQ]; 2010 [June 4]; Available at: http://www.ahrq.gov/news/kt/red/readmissionslides/readslides-contents.htm

23. Kaiser Family Foundation. Summary of key changes to Medicare in 2010 health reform law. Washington DC, 2010. Available at: http://www.kff.org/healthreform/7948.cfm

24. Woods ER, Bhaumik U, Sommer SJ, et al. Community asthma initiative: Evaluation of a quality improvement program for comprehensive asthma care. Pediatrics. 2012;129(3):465-72.

25. Gawande A. The hot spotters. New Yorker. 2011 Jan. 24.Available at: http://www.newyorker.com/reporting/2011/01/24/110124fa_fact_gawande

26. Dwyer J. After boy's death, hospital alters discharging procedures. New York Times. 2012 July 18.Available at: http://www.nytimes.com/2012/07/19/nyregion/after-rory-stauntons-death-hospital-alters-discharge-procedures.html

27. Centers for Disease Control and Prevention [CDC]. Vital signs: Central line-associated blood stream infections--United States, 2001, 2008, and 2009. MMWR Morb Mortal Wkly Rep. 2011;60(8):243-8.

28. Qaseem A, Alguire P, Dallas P, et al. Appropriate use of screening and diagnostic tests to foster high-value, cost-conscious care. Ann Intern Med. 2012;156(2):147-9.

29. Smith-Bindman R, Miglioretti DL, Johnson E, et al. Use of diagnostic imaging studies and associated radiation exposure for patients enrolled in large integrated health care systems, 1996-2010. JAMA. 2012;307(22):2400-9.

30. Hubbard RA, Kerlikowske K, Flowers CI, et al. Cumulative probability of false-positive recall or biopsy recommendation after 10 years of screening mammography: A cohort study. Ann Intern Med. 2011;155(8):481-92.

31. Gawande A. The cost conundrum. New Yorker. 2009 Jun. 1:36-44.Available at: http://www.newyorker.com/reporting/2009/06/01/090601fa_fact_gawande

32. Fisher ES, Wennberg DE, Stukel TA, et al. Variations in the longitudinal efficiency of academic medical centers. Health Aff (Millwood). 2004;Suppl Variation:VAR19-32.

33. Health Care Incentives Improvement Institute. Improving incentives. Newtown, CT, 2012 Jan. Available at: http://www.hci3.org/content/improving-incentives-newsletter-bundled-payment-initiative-stockholm-produces-promising-resu

34. Waldman P. Silicon valley surgeons risk 'moral authority' for 200% returns. Bloomberg Businessweek. 2012 July 19.Available at:

http://www.businessweek.com/news/2012-07-19/silicon-valley-surgeons-risk-moral-authority-for-200-percent-returns

35. Woolhandler S, Campbell T, Himmelstein DU. Costs of health care administration in the United States and Canada. N Engl J Med. 2003;349(8):768-75.

36. Gupta S. More treatment, more mistakes. New York Times. 2012 July 31.Available at: http://www.nytimes.com/2012/08/01/opinion/more-treatment-more-mistakes.html

37. Mello MM, Chandra A, Gawande AA, et al. National costs of the medical liability system. Health Aff (Millwood). 2010;29(9):1569-77.

38. Mello MM, Brennan TA. The role of medical liability reform in federal health care reform. N Engl J Med. 2009;361(1):1-3.

39. Toussaint J. Potent medicine: The collaborative cure for healthcare. Appleton, WI: ThedaCare Center for Healthcare Value; 2012.

40. Toussaint J. Writing the new playbook for U.S. Health care: Lessons from wisconsin. Health Aff (Millwood). 2009;28(5):1343-50.

41. Centers for Medicare and Medicaid Services [CMS]. National health expenditure projections 2011-2021. Baltimore, MD: Office of the Actuary, 2012. Available at: https://http://www.cms.gov/Research-Statistics-Data-and-Systems/Statistics-Trends-and-Reports/NationalHealthExpendData/NationalHealthAccountsProjected.html

42. Altman SH. The lessons of Medicare's prospective payment system show that the bundled payment program faces challenges. Health Aff (Millwood). 2012;31(9):1923-30.

43. Smith TA, Bookson ST. Hospital billing errors can send you to the poorhouse. Medical Billing Advocates of America.

2011.Available at:
http://www.billadvocates.com/index.php?option=com_easyblog&vie
w=entry&id=16&Itemid=131

44. Bernard TS. Getting lost in the labyrinth of medical bills. New
York Times. 2012 June 22.Available at:
http://www.nytimes.com/2012/06/23/your-money/health-
insurance/navigating-the-labyrinth-of-medical-costs-your-
money.html

45. Berenson R. Out of whack: Pricing distortions in the Medicare
physician fee schedule. National Institute for Health Care
Management Foundation, 2010 Sept. Available at:
http://www.nihcm.org/component/content/article/405

46. American Academy of Family Physicians [AAFP]. Family
physician workforce reform: Recommendations of the American
Academy of Family Physicians. 2012. Available at:
http://www.aafp.org/online/en/home/policy/policies/w/workforce.ht
ml

47. U.S. Government Accountability Office [GAO]. Medicare: Lack
of price transparency may hamper hospitals' ability to be prudent
purchasers of implantable medical devices. Washington DC, 2012
Jan. Report No.: GAO-12-126. Available at:
http://www.gao.gov/products/GAO-12-126

48. Bennett A. The cost of hope: A memoir. New York: Random
House Incorporated; 2012.

49. Centers for Medicare and Medicaid Services [CMS]. Medicare
acute care episode demonstration for orthopedic and cardiovascular
surgery. Baltimore, MD, 2012. Available at:
http://www.cms.gov/Medicare/Demonstration-
Projects/DemoProjectsEvalRpts/Medicare-Demonstrations-
Items/CMS1204388.html

50. Mechanic RE. Opportunities and challenges for episode-based
payment. N Engl J Med. 2011;365(9):777-9.

51. Vesely R. An ace in the deck? Bundled-payment demo shows returns. Modern Healthcare. 2011;41(6):32-3.

52. Centers for Medicare and Medicaid Services [CMS]. Competitive bidding update—one year implementation update. Baltimore, MD, 2012 Apr 17. Available at: http://www.cms.gov/Medicare/Medicare-Fee-for-Service-Payment/DMEPOSCompetitiveBid/

53. Silver RM, Landon MB, Rouse DJ, et al. Maternal morbidity associated with multiple repeat cesarean deliveries. Obstet Gynecol. 2006;107(6):1226-32.

54. Smith GC, Pell JP, Dobbie R. Caesarean section and risk of unexplained stillbirth in subsequent pregnancy. Lancet. 2003;362(9398):1779-84.

55. U.S. Government Accountability Office [GAO]. Meaningful price information is difficult for consumers to obtain prior to receiving care. Washington DC, 2011 Sept. 23. Report No.: GAO-11-791. Available at: http://www.gao.gov/products/GAO-11-791

56. Topol EJ. The creative destruction of medicine: How the digital revolution will create better health care. New York: Basic Books; 2012.

57. Christensen C. When giants fail: What business has learned from Clayton Christensen. New Yorker. 2012 May 14.Available at: http://www.newyorker.com/reporting/2012/05/14/120514fa_fact_macfarquhar

58. Christensen C. Health care: The simple solution. Bloomberg Businessweek. 2010 Mar. 4.Available at: http://www.businessweek.com/magazine/content/10_11/b4170072396095.htm

59. Institute of Medicine [IOM]. The future of nursing: Leading change, advancing health. Washington DC: National Academies Press, 2011. Report No.: 0309158192. Available at:

http://www.iom.edu/Reports/2010/The-Future-of-Nursing-Leading-Change-Advancing-Health.aspx

60. Medicare Payment Advisory Commission (MedPAC). Report to Congress: Medicare and the health care delivery system. Washington DC, 2012 June. Available at: http://medpac.gov/documents/Jun12_EntireReport.pdf

61. de Brantes F, Rastogi A, Painter M. Reducing potentially avoidable complications in patients with chronic diseases: The Prometheus payment approach. Health Serv Res. 2010;45(6 Pt 2):1854-71.

62. Campaign Finance Institute. The cost of winning a house and senate seat, 1986-2010. Vital Statistics on Congress, 2012. Available at: http://cfinst.org/data.aspx

63. Frates C. Exclusive: AHIP gave more than $100 million to chamber's efforts to derail health care reform. National Journal. 2012 June 13.Available at: http://www.nationaljournal.com/blogs/influencealley/2012/06/exclusive-ahip-gave-more-than-100-million-to-chamber-s-efforts-to-derail-health-care-reform-13

64. Health Affairs, Robert Wood Johnson Foundation. Next steps for ACOs. 2012 Jan. 31. Available at: http://www.healthaffairs.org/healthpolicybriefs/brief.php?brief_id=61

65. Berwick DM. Making good on ACOs' promise - the final rule for the Medicare shared savings program. N Engl J Med. 2011.

66. Farrell KS, Finocchio LJ, Trivedi AN, et al. Does price transparency legislation allow the uninsured to shop for care? J Gen Intern Med. 2010;25(2):110-4.

About the Authors and Contributors

François de Brantes is Executive Director of the Health Care Incentives Improvement Institute where he leads the organization's efforts to accelerate the transformation of the health care industry into delivering greater value. François has been published in a number of journals including the New England Journal of Medicine, Health Affairs, the American Journal of Managed Care, and some of his work has been featured in articles in the New York Times and the Wall Street Journal. He can be reached at francois.debrantes@hci3.org.

Bob Conte is a business writer, editor, and communications consultant. He works with a broad range of local, national and global clients, and has received many industry awards for his work across the communications spectrum. Bob is also the author of a textbook on American music. He can be reached at bob@bobconte.com.

Kriss Wittmann is the principal artist at Wittmann Studios, a firm that specializes in creating illustrations that translate complex concepts into simple pictures. She can be reached at kwittm01@comcast.net.

John Milano designed the cover and is an experienced and accomplished graphic designer. He can be reached at john@designers-touch.net.

Jenna T. Sirkin is a health services researcher at the Schneider Institutes for Health Policy, Brandeis University and co-author of the book, *Breaking the poverty cycle: The human basis for sustainable development.* She can be reached at jsirkin@brandeis.edu.

Made in the USA
Middletown, DE
04 June 2020